THE PEASANT AND THE DONKEY

Tales of the Near and Middle East

THE PEASANT AND

THE DONKEY

Tales of the Near and Middle East

H. M. Nahmad

with stories by Charles Downing,
Nadia Abu-Zahra, Feyyaz Kayacan, and Mary Fergar

illustrated by William Papas

New York   Henry Z. Walck, Incorporated   1968

Contents

THE NIGHTINGALE HAZARAN (Armenian), 9
by Charles Downing

SHAH ABBAS AND THE COBBLER (Persian), 15
by H. M. Nahmad

THE PILGRIM AND THE JUDGE (Arabic), 19
by H. M. Nahmad

THE RED SLIPPERS OF HONEIM (Hebrew-Jewish), 22
by H. M. Nahmad

SAINT MICHAEL AND THE IDLE HUSBAND (Arabic), 28
by H. M. Nahmad

THE TEACHER AND HIS PUPIL (Arabic), 33
by H. M. Nahmad

THE PEASANT AND THE DONKEY (Turkish), 34
by Feyyaz Kayacan and Mary Fergar

THE MERCHANT'S SON AND THE SLAVE (Hebrew-Jewish), 40
by H. M. Nahmad

THE APE AND THE TWO CATS (Arabic), 42
by H. M. Nahmad

A LIE FOR A LIE (Arabic), 43
by H. M. Nahmad

THE BEARDLESS, THE LAME, AND THE
ONE-EYED THIEF (Armenian), 45
by Charles Downing

THE KING WHO TRIED TO CHEAT DESTINY (Arabic), 53
by H. M. Nahmad

MAIMONIDES AND THE BOTTLE OF POISON (Hebrew-Jewish), 60
by H. M. Nahmad

THE CLEVER BRIDE OF TUNISIA (Arabic), 61
by Nadia Abu-Zahra

BADIKAN AND KHAN BOGHU (Armenian), 68
by Charles Downing

THE COVETOUS MINISTER (Hebrew-Jewish), 76
by H. M. Nahmad

TWO WATERMELON STORIES (Turkish), 79
by Feyyaz Kayacan and Mary Fergar

HANI THE SIMPLE (Arabic), 83
by H. M. Nahmad

THE GOLDSMITH, THE WOOD CARVER, THE
TAILOR, AND THE HERMIT WHO QUARRELED
OVER A WOODEN WOMAN (Persian), 90
by H. M. Nahmad

THE KING AND THE TWO OWLS (Arabic), 95
by H. M. Nahmad

THE STUPID HUNTER AND THE CRAFTY BIRD (Hebrew-Jewish), 97
by H. M. Nahmad

THE THREE APPLES (Turkish), 99
by Feyyaz Kayacan and Mary Fergar

MASTER AND PUPIL (Georgian), 104
by Charles Downing

THE FOWLER, THE PARROT, AND THE KING (Persian), 110
by H. M. Nahmad

THREE TIMES LUCKY (Arabic), 113
by H. M. Nahmad

THE STORY OF THE BOY WHO COULDN'T KEEP
ANYTHING IN HIS HEAD (Turkish), 123
by Feyyaz Kayacan and Mary Fergar

THE TALE OF A PROVERB (Arabic), 130
by Nadia Abu-Zahra

THE DONKEY, THE OX, AND THE FARMER (Hebrew-Jewish), 132
by H. M. Nahmad

JUHA AND THE DISPUTE OVER A GOAT (Arabic), 137
by H. M. Nahmad

JUHA AT THE BANQUET (Arabic), 140
by H. M. Nahmad

THE MAGIC DAGGER (Turkish), 141
by Feyyaz Kayacan and Mary Fergar

ZOHAIR AND THE WITCH (Arabic), 147
by H. M. Nahmad

"CAST THY BREAD UPON THE WATERS" (Hebrew-Jewish), 151
by H. M. Nahmad

HEART AND MIND (Armenian), 155
by Charles Downing

The Nightingale Hazaran

There was and there wasn't, there was once a king, and this king decided to build a magnificent church. For seven years his men built. The church was finished, and the bishop consecrated it, when suddenly a great wind blew. The king was gasping for breath, when it suddenly subsided, and in front of him he saw a hermit.

"Long life to you, O King!" said the hermit. "You have built a fine temple, but there is one thing missing."

The wind blew fiercely, and the hermit disappeared.

The king ordered the church to be demolished, and his men began again. For another seven years they worked, and there again stood a magnificent church, more beautiful than the first. The bishop consecrated it, the king knelt to pray, when a mighty wind blew through the nave. The hermit stood again before the king.

"Long life to you, O King!" said the hermit. "You have again built a fine church, but there is one thing missing."

Once again the king ordered the church to be demolished.

"This time," he said, "we shall build for nine years. There shall not be its like on earth."

9

It was built. It was consecrated. The king knelt to pray. A tempest blew through the church, and again the hermit stood before him.

"Long life to you, O King!" said the hermit. "Your church has not its like on earth. It is a pity that there is one thing missing."

The king was desperate. He seized the hermit by the arm.

"This is the third time you make me destroy my church," he said. "Tell me, what is missing?"

"The nightingale Hazaran," replied the hermit, and disappeared.

The king returned to his palace. He had three sons.

"I must acquire the nightingale Hazaran for my church," he said. "But how shall I find it?"

"We shall find it," said his sons. And they mounted their horses and rode away.

After a month they came to a place where the road forked in three directions, and there they stopped, undecided what to do.

A hermit approached them.

"Where are you going, my brave fellows?" he said.

"We are looking for the nightingale Hazaran," said the princes. "But we do not know which road to take."

"He who takes the first road," said the hermit, "shall return. He who takes the second road may return, or not. He who takes the third has little hope of returning."

The eldest brother took the first road, the widest; the second brother took the middle road; the youngest brother chose the third road, the narrowest.

"Why have I little hope of returning?" he asked the hermit.

"It is a road beset with hazards," said the hermit. "You will come first to a river. The mistress of the nightingale Hazaran has cast a spell on it and polluted it, and she will not drink from its waters. To pass it, you must drink from it, and say, 'Ah! The waters of life!' Thus you will cross the river. Then you will come to a flower. The sorceress has changed it into a thistle, but you must pick it, smell it, and exclaim, 'O flower of paradise!' As you go on, you will come to a wolf and a lamb tied to posts near each other; in front of the wolf lies a heap of grass, in front of the lamb a piece of meat. You must give the grass to the lamb, the meat to the wolf. Farther on you will come to a pair of huge gates; one will be shut, the other open. You must shut the open one, and open the shut one. As you enter the gates, you will behold the mistress of the nightingale Hazaran. For seven days she sleeps, for seven days she wakes. If you are able to do all the things I have told you, you will bring back the nightingale Hazaran; if not, you will not return."

The eldest brother journeyed along the wide road until he came to a palace.

"Why should I look for trouble?" he said. "I will offer my services to the lord of this palace, and will live a quiet life."

The second brother journeyed along the second road, crossed over a hill, and saw a palace burning like a torch. He dismounted and tethered his horse, went into a pleasant garden and sat down on the soft green grass. Suddenly he beheld an enormous black Arab walking between heaven and earth. The Arab swooped down on the prince, struck him with his whip, and turned him into a round stone, which rolled under a garden seat.

The youngest brother journeyed along the third road, and as the hermit had foretold, met with the river, the flower, the wolf and the lamb. He entered the palace, and saw, lying on a divan, a maiden as fair and graceful as a roe deer. The nightingale Hazaran fluttered out of his cage, alighted on the maiden's bosom, and began to pour out a thousand lullabies. The maiden fell asleep, and the prince quickly grasped the nightingale, kissed the maiden on the cheek, and made his way back along the narrow road.

The maiden awoke after seven days, and suddenly saw that her nightingale had vanished.

"Gates, seize him!" she cried.

"God go with him," said the gates. "He closed our open side and opened our closed side, and gave us great relief."

"Wolf and lamb, seize the thief!" cried the maiden again.

"God go with him," said the wolf and the lamb. "He gave grass to the lamb, and meat to the wolf."

"Thistle, stop him!" cried the maiden.

"God go with him," replied the thistle. "You turned me into a thistle. For him I was a flower of paradise."

"River, stop him!" she cried.

"God go with him," said the river. "You turned me into a noxious stream, but for him I was the waters of life."

The maiden leaped onto her horse.

In the meantime, the prince had come to the end of the

road, where he found the old hermit waiting for him. He inquired after his brothers.

"They have not come back," said the hermit.

The prince entrusted the nightingale Hazaran to his care, and galloped up the wide road. When he came to the large city, he went to the inn for a meal. There was his elder brother, working as a servant. He told him of the success of his mission, and took him back to the crossroads, where he left him in the care of the hermit. Then he went off in search of his other brother. Like him, he came to the palace which burned like a torch. He dismounted, and went into a garden to lie on the soft green grass. Suddenly the huge black Arab swooped down upon him.

"Who said this grass was free for you to sit on?" said the Arab, and aimed a blow at the prince with his whip. But the prince was too fast for him and, wrenching the whip from the Arab's grasp, he struck him with it instead. The Arab was immediately turned into a stone.

"That is what must have happened to my brother," thought the prince, and began to whip at the stones at his feet. The stones were suddenly transformed into human beings, who began to make off in all directions. He struck the last stone beneath the bench where he was sitting, and his brother appeared and made to run away.

"Don't run away, brother," he called, and telling him of his successful mission, he accompanied him also to the crossroads. Here the three brothers took the nightingale Hazaran from the hermit, and made their way home.

13

On the way they came to a well and, being thirsty, they lowered their youngest brother down into the well so that he might hand them up a bowl of water. While he was still down the well, the eldest brother said to the second brother, "If he comes with us to tell our father the king what happened, how shall we look?"

So they left their youngest brother down the well, and brought the nightingale to their father.

"Our younger brother has perished," they said. "But we have brought you the nightingale Hazaran."

The king placed the nightingale in the church, and not only would he not sing, he barely breathed.

Soon afterward the maiden came riding up to the king.

"Who was the brave youth who took my nightingale?" she said.

"We took it," said the two brothers.

"What did you encounter on the way?" asked the maiden.

"Nothing," said the brothers.

"You did not take it," she said. "You are liars and thieves."

And she seized them, and their father the king, and threw them into a dungeon. Then she seized the whole town and began to rule over it herself, vowing that they should never again be free until she had seen the brave youth who had taken the nightingale.

In the meantime some harvesters had drawn the young prince out of the well. When he came to the king's palace, he saw neither his father nor his two brothers; but the townsfolk told him what had happened, and the young man went straight to the dungeon, and released his father and two brothers. As they left the dungeon the maiden came upon them.

"I am the mistress of the nightingale Hazaran," she said. "Are you not afraid?"

"I am the one who took the nightingale Hazaran from you," said the prince. "Why should I be afraid?"

"What did you encounter on the way?" said the maiden.

The young man told of the river, the thistle, the wolf, the lamb, the gates, and all that he had seen and done.

"And while you were sleeping, I kissed you on the cheek," he concluded, "and now I claim you as my bride."

The maiden held him to be worthy of her, and consented, and they were married in the king's magnificent church. And how the nightingale Hazaran sang there, pouring out a stream of a thousand melodies, how he sang!

Three apples fell from heaven, one for the storyteller, one for his listener, and one for him who lends an ear.

Shah Abbas and the Cobbler

Shah Abbas was a just and righteous king who ruled Persia many years ago. It is related that he used to spend his evenings wandering through the streets of his capital in the guise of a holy man. He did this, it is said, in order to find out how the poor and humble among his people lived.

One evening the Shah in his disguise stopped outside a small cottage on the outskirts of the city and begged admittance. He was asked in by a poorly-dressed man who invited his unexpected visitor to share his simple meal. The man was a cheerful and talkative person, and he entertained his guest with lively and witty conversation. After a while Shah Abbas asked his host what he did for a living.

"I am a cobbler," answered the man. "During the day I busy myself mending people's shoes in various parts of the town. With the money I earn from cobbling I buy food for my evening meal."

"Do you not concern yourself with the morrow?" asked Shah Abbas.

"God will provide," was the cobbler's reply.

When it grew late the king got up to go. Before he left he promised the cobbler that he would come and see him again on the following evening.

Next morning the king issued an edict forbidding shoe repairers to follow their calling without a royal permit. When he visited the cobbler again in the evening he found him at his meal, eating and drinking with enjoyment.

"How went your work today, my friend?" asked Shah Abbas.

The cobbler replied, "As I was walking through the streets of the city this morning I heard that the king had forbidden the cobblers to follow their trade without a permit. So I went to the cloth market and found work as a porter, and so earned enough money to provide for my needs."

"But supposing tomorrow our lord the king forbids people to work as porters in the markets, what will you do then?" asked Shah Abbas.

"God will provide," was the cobbler's reply.

On the following morning the king prohibited working as a porter in the markets without royal permission. That same evening he visited the cobbler, who was having his supper as usual.

"And what did you do today?" asked Shah Abbas after they had exchanged greetings. "I heard that our king forbade the porters to work in the markets without permission."

"I went around chopping wood for people, and in that way earned enough for my needs."

"And what if tomorrow the chopping of wood is forbidden?"

"God will provide," was the cobbler's reply.

Shah Abbas then left after promising to come back the following evening.

Next morning the king's herald proclaimed that all wood choppers were to be conscripted into the royal guard. The cobbler went to the palace where they gave him a sword and put him on guard duty. When evening came he took the sword to a shopkeeper where he pledged the sword blade, and with the money he got he bought some food for his evening meal, and went home. There he took a piece of wood and fashioned a blade out of it; then he fixed it to the sword hilt and put it in its sheath.

Soon afterward Shah Abbas, in his usual disguise, paid his evening visit to the cobbler. Again, as usual, the king asked his humble host what work he had done that day.

"I was put on guard at the palace," said the cobbler, "and so earned no money. So I was obliged to pledge the sword blade in order to buy the food we are now eating. In its place I made a wooden blade."

"What will you do if there is a sword inspection tomorrow?" asked Shah Abbas.

"As God wills," came the reply.

On the following morning, when the cobbler reported for duty at the palace, the officer of the guard handed over a prisoner to him, saying, "This man is under sentence of death; you are ordered to behead him."

"I cannot kill him," protested the cobbler. "I cannot shed the blood of any man."

But his protests and pleadings were in vain. He was told that it was a command and that he must obey. So the poor cobbler grasped his sword and, turning his face to the crowd gathered for the execution, proclaimed in a loud voice,

"I swear to you by the name of the Almighty that I am not a murderer and cannot slay this man. If it be decreed that the prisoner shall die, let my sword be of steel; but if he be innocent, then let the blade be turned into wood!"

With these words he unsheathed the blade and, behold, it

18

was of wood. At this sight the assembled people stood in awe and wonderment, for it was as if they were witnessing a miracle.

When news of what had happened reached Shah Abbas he called the cobbler before him. Revealing his true identity, the king embraced the cobbler. He praised him not only for his shrewdness and quick wit, but also for his steadfast faith. To show his appreciation of his humble friend, Shah Abbas appointed the cobbler to a high position in the royal court and made him an adviser and counselor.

The Pilgrim and the Judge

A man, who was making a pilgrimage, stopped on his way at a city to stay for a short while with a friend. When his stay came to an end and he was about to set out again on his journey, he confided to his friend that he had some money and jewels which he wanted to leave with a trustworthy person until his return. Now the pilgrim's friend was shy of asking his guest to leave the valuables with him for fear that he might be suspected of coveting them, so he advised him to leave the money and jewels with a certain judge in that city.

Next morning the pilgrim went to the judge and told him

that he wanted to leave his property with him for safekeeping until his return from the pilgrimage. The judge promised faithfully to look after it until the pilgrim's return. Handing him a key, the judge said, "Take this key and open that chest over there; put your money and jewels into it, then lock it securely." This the pilgrim did, and handed back the key to the judge. He then thanked the judge, bade him farewell, and departed on his journey.

After some weeks the pilgrim returned and went right away to the judge's house to take back his money and jewels. But the judge pretended not to know the pilgrim and denied all knowledge of ever having received any money or jewels for safekeeping.

The angry and bewildered pilgrim went to his friend and told him what had happened, and blamed him for his advice. The friend thereupon took the pilgrim with him to one of the king's sons, who was known for his wisdom in settling disputes, and told him what had happened. The prince promised the two friends that he would go the very next day to see the judge. He also advised the pilgrim to go to the judge's house again at a certain hour on the afternoon of the following day—when the prince would be present—and ask for his property back.

The next day the prince called on the judge, who greeted him according to his exalted rank and said he hoped the royal visit boded good for him and his house. The prince, after assuring the judge that all was well and that he had nothing to fear, said,

"Last night, after the royal council had ended and the

people attending it had left, my father the king asked me to stay behind as he had some matters of importance to discuss with me. He said that he wished to make the pilgrimage in the coming year—which will soon be upon us— and wanted to hand over, in his absence, the kingdom to a reliable and trustworthy person who would look after it and keep it safe until the king's return from the pilgrimage. He sought my advice on the matter, so I advised him to entrust the kingdom to your Honor on account of your uprightness and trustworthiness, rather than to one of the notables, who might covet the kingdom and cause sedition among the king's subjects. My advice pleased His Majesty greatly, and he decided to call a general council to do what I advised."

When the judge heard these words he rejoiced, and praised the king's wisdom and sagacity in extravagant language. At that very moment the pilgrim entered the judge's office, and after greeting both the prince and the judge in accordance with custom, he announced that he had come for the jewels and the money he had deposited with the judge before setting out on his pilgrimage. The judge returned the pilgrim's greeting and said,

"Yes, yes, my friend; I had a dream during the night in which I saw both you and your deposit, and I remembered well your coming. Here is the key. Go and unlock the chest, take your property, and go in peace."

The pilgrim took his money and jewels, thanked the judge, and departed. Soon afterward the prince also left.

Some weeks passed without the judge's hearing any further from the prince, and he began to grow anxious. So one day he went to the palace and asked the prince when the king would be making the necessary arrangements for the handing over of the kingdom to him.

"Your Honor," said the prince in reply, "we did not know how to get back from you the property of the pilgrim, who was a stranger in our land, except by giving you possession of the entire kingdom. But if we handed it over to you for temporary safekeeping, how should we get it back when the time was up?"

The judge went away, angry at having been tricked by the prince, but reflecting that he had only his own greed and dishonesty to blame.

The Red Slippers of Honeim

Many many years ago, in a market town of Syria, there lived a shoemaker by the name of Honeim. He was a modest and humble man who spoke little but worked hard to keep himself and his wife and family. A skilled craftsman, he was famed far and wide for the excellence of his shoes and slippers, which were made of the finest leather. People came from all over the country to purchase Honeim's shoes.

One day Honeim made a pair of slippers of soft bright-red leather sewn with an embroidered pattern of fine gold thread. They were of exquisite workmanship, and by far the best pair of slippers he had ever made in the whole of his life. The red of their leather glowed like a lamp in the dusk, and the gold-thread pattern glittered like a precious jewel. They were small and elegant; fit to grace the foot of a prince's bride. The little shoemaker gazed for a long time at the slippers he had made, as if undecided whether to part with them or not. Finally he made up his mind not to sell them; he would keep them. But he put them on a stall with the other shoes and slippers, and every now and then during the day he would lift his eyes from his last and look for a while at the red leather slippers.

It was not very long before people heard of these beautiful red slippers Honeim had made, and they flocked from miles around to look at them and admire them, and tell other people about them. One day a richly-attired young man, mounted on a fine Arabian horse, rode up and stopped outside Honeim's shop. He rested his eyes for a few moments on the red slippers. "These exquisite red slippers," he said to himself, "would be a fitting gift for my bride. I shall buy them."

So saying, he dismounted and strode over to where Honeim was busy at his last.

"I want to buy that pair of red slippers. What is their price?" he demanded haughtily.

"I am sorry, my master; but those slippers are not for sale," replied the shoemaker quietly, concealing his anger at the young man's arrogant tone.

And no amount of cajoling, threatening, haggling and bargaining on the part of the rich young man could persuade Honeim to part with the slippers. In the end, angry and disappointed at not getting his own way, he jumped onto his horse and rode swiftly away. As the only son of his father, who was a rich merchant, nothing that he asked for was ever denied him. He was determined to get the red leather slippers, however much he had to pay for them. He made up his mind to go back to the market, where the shop was, the following day. Next morning he was back at the shop, demanding the red slippers. From the inside of his robe the young man pulled out a purse filled with gold coins, but Honeim would not be tempted. He would not part with the slippers; they were not for sale, he repeated. Angered at his failure a second time, the merchant's son left the shop, but not before promising to return again and again until he got possession of the red slippers.

That night, after their evening meal, the shoemaker's wife remonstrated with her husband over the red slippers.

"Why don't you sell them to this man?" she asked. "He is willing to pay you a good price for them. Let him have them; otherwise he will come day after day worrying you until he gets them. His father is a powerful man, he lives in a house which is like a palace, and he has as many servants as a prince. And, anyway, why do you slave from morning to night, if not to sell the wares you produce by your own hands?"

The quiet shoemaker did not answer his wife; for how could he tell her that the red slippers were not destined for the rich man's son, nor, indeed, for any other passing buyer? How could he tell her that they would wait for the right person to claim them? She would not understand; she would think him mad. So he muttered something to her about their being too beautiful to sell.

The following morning, in accordance with his promise, the young man rode up and dismounted in front of Honeim's shop. Again he demanded to buy the red slippers. This time Honeim did not refuse him. He knew that if he did he would get no peace, neither from his wife nor from the young man. His customer paid the price asked for the slippers, took them and rode off in triumph. For some time afterward, the shoe-maker gazed at the space where the red slippers had once stood, shrugged his shoulders in a gesture of resignation, and went back to his last and needle and thread.

Early next morning there was a commotion in the house of the rich merchant; for on awakening at sunrise his son had found that one of the red slippers—the right one—had disappeared. The great house was searched from top to bottom; the servants were questioned, and the news was spread abroad that a cunning thief had broken into the house at night and stolen one of the red slippers. The young man was wild with rage. He threatened the servants with a beating if the lost slipper was not found by sunset. Suddenly he thought of the quiet shoemaker. Perhaps the cunning rascal had stolen back the slipper. He would find out. So he had his horse saddled and rode at breakneck speed to Honeim's shop.

On arrival there, he found the shoemaker at his usual

place on the workbench. Honeim gave his visitor a brief greeting and went on with his work. The merchant's son looked around the shop and at all the shoes and slippers and pieces of leather there, but of the single red slipper he had lost there was no trace. He questioned the shoemaker, but with no result. Honeim knew nothing of the missing slipper and could not help him.

Dejected and disappointed, the young man rode home. Perhaps when he got back, he thought, the lovely red slipper would already have been found. But, alas, when he reached his father's house, he learned that the slipper had still not been found. The rich merchant announced that he would pay a handsome reward to anybody who could find the lost slipper. His son's disappointment turned to anger, and he carried out his threat to beat his servants. He then went into his room, and for a long time gazed at the solitary red slipper, now bereft of its companion. Its soft red leather seemed to glow with even a brighter light than before, and the pattern of gold thread glittered against the rich furnishings of the room.

That night a guard was put over the slipper that remained; but the next morning that, too, had gone. The guard was brought before the merchant's son, and beaten and thrown into prison without food. The wretched man confessed that he had fallen asleep for a few minutes during the night, and that when he had awakened, the slipper had gone. Again, the great house was searched from top to bottom, but to no avail. The second red slipper had gone the way of the first, and it was never found.

26

The young man could not understand what had happened. Neither harsh punishment nor promise of a rich reward had brought back the red slippers. They had just vanished into thin air as if a spell had been laid upon them by some magician or malevolent spirit. There was only one thing to do, he told himself, and that was to get the shoemaker to sew him another pair of red slippers exactly the same as those he had lost, so that nobody would be able to tell the difference between them. He had to have them, for he was a proud and arrogant man who boasted before all his fellows that he always got what he wanted.

The same morning he went to the shoemaker's shop in the town market. Honeim greeted the merchant's son briefly and, taking a gold coin from the counter, handed it to him. Before the young man could open his mouth to utter a word, the shoemaker spoke.

"I know from your face what you have come for. You have come for the slippers, but they are not here, nor will you ever find them; for they were not destined for you. In vain I told you that they were not for sale, but you would not listen. Not all your gold and riches will buy you another pair of red slippers like those you have lost. Take back the money you paid for them, master, and go in peace."

After that, the merchant's son knew that it would be no use arguing with the shoemaker or asking him to make another pair of red slippers. He mounted his horse, but did not return home, for he could not bear to face the taunts and jeers of the people when they heard the story of the red slippers. He went to another country where he was not known, and was never seen again. The shoemaker continued to make the finest shoes and slippers, but to the day he died, which was many years later, he was never heard to mention the red slippers again, and thus nobody was ever able to learn their secret, or for whom they were made.

Long after these events had taken place people continued to relate the strange story of the red slippers. And to this very day, whenever anyone is sent on a fool's errand, or returns empty-handed, they say of him that he has come back with Honeim's slippers.

Saint Michael and the Idle Husband

There once lived in a village near the city of Beirut a very poor man and his wife. The man was a lazy and idle fellow who avoided work of any kind. He spent much of the day in sleep or lounging about. His wife, a patient and uncomplaining woman, worked hard to earn the bare necessities of life for the two of them. She bore her lot with fortitude; but one day the poor woman felt that she had had enough of her husband's idle ways. Finding him asleep long after the sun had risen, she began to abuse him for his sloth.

"You lazy good-for-nothing," she shouted. "Why don't

you get up and find some work to do and earn a few piasters for yourself like everybody else, instead of lying in bed half the day? Upon my life, I know of no one as lazy as you in the whole of this city. Do you know what people say about you? They say that you would rather die of hunger than turn your hand to an honest day's work. Aren't you ashamed of yourself?"

The husband, angry at being so rudely awakened, shouted back at his wife, "Be silent, you shrew! What sort of talk is this? I have not worked since I was a boy, and I do not intend to start now."

With that, he walked out of the mean hut, which was their home, muttering to himself. "Am I not always praying to Saint Michael to help me?" he grumbled.

Now it was quite true that the poor man prayed continually to the Saint to lighten his lot in life, but nothing seemed to come of his prayers. Perhaps Saint Michael did not hear him; or perhaps, on the other hand, he paid no attention.

That very same night, however, when the man was asleep, Saint Michael appeared to him in a dream and said,

"My son, why are you so idle, why don't you bestir yourself instead of repeatedly asking me to do something for you to keep you from hunger? Are you not ashamed of your behavior? Go out and find some work and earn a little money. Do this, and I shall surely help you. I shall not forsake you." Having thus spoken, Saint Michael disappeared.

The man awoke from his sleep, perplexed and disturbed by his strange dream. At last he closed his eyes and went off to sleep again. A second time Saint Michael appeared to him and said,

"My son, why do you continue to lead a life of idleness and sloth? Have I not told you that you must work for your living? Now listen to what I am about to tell you. Tomorrow at sunrise get up and go down to the city where I will guide you to the house of a certain rich man. Say to him, 'I want some money as a loan to set myself up as a merchant.' If he says that he wants some person to be surety for you, tell him that the Archangel Michael will be a surety and will stand witness for both you and him. When he hears these words he will let you have the money."

The following morning at sunrise the man got up, washed, and swallowed a morsel of bread, and went down to the rich man's house in the town, guided thither by Saint Michael, and did what had been commanded him in the dream. The rich man gave him three hundred dinars; then he asked who would be surety for the loan and testify for the poor man.

"The Archangel Michael will be my surety and will testify for me," replied the man.

"When will you repay me the money?" the rich man asked.

"Next year, on the eighth day of November, I will pay you back the money and the interest on it."

The man took the money and went away and bought some goods. These he loaded onto a ship, and the next morning set sail for a distant land. There he sold the goods he had bought, and with the profit on their sale bought more goods. His enterprise and industry brought him reward, and he prospered greatly. So busy was he that he did not notice the passage of time, until one day he realized that the payment of the loan fell due in two days' time. What could he do to repay the debt to his benefactor? he asked himself. It was a voyage of forty days back to his native land.

After a lot of thought he hit upon an idea. He went and got himself some lead and made from it a box. In it he placed six hundred dinars: the three hundred he had borrowed, and three hundred he had added as interest. He then sealed the box and wrote on it the name of Saint Michael, his own name, and that of the rich man. Having done this, he addressed himself to Saint Michael, saying, "O Saint Michael, you did help me and tell me what to do; you testified on my behalf before the rich man who lent me the money. And now I am sending you the money so that you may return it with interest to the lender."

After that he threw the box into the sea on the seventh day of November, about nine o'clock on the eve of the Feast of Saint Michael. He had no sooner cast the box into the water when it was swallowed up by a large whale. With the Saint's help and guidance the great fish covered the forty days' journey to Beirut in the twinkling of an eye.

Now it was the rich man's custom to celebrate Saint Michael's Day every year. On the eve of the festival he used to order some fishermen to go out and catch the festival whales. This they did; but that year they caught only the whale which had swallowed the lead box. They took it to the rich man's house and cut open its stomach. In it they found something that looked like a large meatball made of lead. The man was greatly astonished at what his eyes beheld.

"God be praised!" he exclaimed in wonder. "This big fish devours everything it finds in the sea." So saying, he put it away in a corner of the house, thinking that it was only a lump of lead of no importance or value.

Two months later the other man returned from his travels with goods and riches. People who knew him were filled with astonishment at his great wealth. Now he was the richest man in the town where once he was the poorest. The man from whom he had borrowed the money soon learned that he was back. When the poor man (for many people still thought of him as that) heard that his benefactor was asking for him, he went straight away to his house, only to be greeted with anger and abuse. Why had he not returned the money when it was due, as he had promised? The poor fellow, taken aback, explained what had happened; how he had put six hundred dinars into a lead box and written on it the name of Saint Michael, his own name, and that of the lender of the money, and then thrown it into the sea, relying on the Saint to deliver it to its destination. The rich man listened in wonder and amazement, and asked when all this had happened.

"On the eve of the Feast of Saint Michael," came the

answer, "the seventh day of November, about nine o'clock."

The rich man then recalled that it was on that very night that the fishermen had caught the whale and found in its belly the lump of lead. He at once had it fetched from a corner of the house, and there, exactly as his visitor said, were the three names written on the box, and the six hundred dinars inside it. The rich man took three hundred dinars and handed them to the other, saying, "Take this money; I do not want the interest from you. Take back also the original sum and donate it to the Church of St. Michael."

After the caller had gone, the rich man wondered at the faith of the poor man who had become rich through the assistance of the Saint. Before long the news of the miracle was common property. It was related how Saint Michael had sent the payment of the debt in the belly of a whale across the seven seas. And for many a long day the people in the surrounding villages never tired of telling the story of the miracle of Saint Michael.

The Teacher and His Pupil

There was once a teacher who used to board one of his pupils. One evening, after they had had their supper, they set out to visit some friends. On the way the teacher asked his pupil if he had remembered to put out the lamp before leaving the house.

"No," answered the pupil, "I forgot."

The teacher said, "Do you know that as a result of your forgetfulness we have lost three *dirhems* this evening?"

"How is that?" asked the pupil.

"Because we left the lamp burning, and by now it will have used up three *dirhems'* worth of oil," replied the teacher.

"Never mind, master," said the pupil. "I shall go back and put it out."

With that he hurried back to the house, put out the lamp, and ran back to his teacher. When he caught up with his teacher the latter said, "And now we have lost even more money than before."

"Why is that?" the pupil asked.

"Because you have worn out at least five *dirhems'* worth of leather off your shoes running to the house and back," was the reply.

"Do not worry about that, master," the pupil said to him. "I carried my shoes under my arm all the way."

The Peasant and the Donkey

Once upon a time, when parrots were hairdressers and I rocked my father's cradle, there was a peasant who lived in a village. One day this peasant took two large baskets, mounted his donkey, and went to a small vineyard he owned some distance away. When he got there he tethered the donkey to a tree and started picking juicy bunches of grapes and, layer by layer, placed them in his baskets. As the baskets were big and deep, it took him quite a long time to fill them up. When they were full, the peasant loaded the baskets onto the donkey and secured them, and then took the road to the nearest town to sell his grapes. Now this town was a ten-hour walk from his vineyard.

After walking for five hours in the blazing sun, the peasant arrived at a fountain. He was now as tired as his donkey and his tongue was as dry as an autumn leaf. He watered the donkey, had a cool, well-deserved drink himself, and sat down under the shade of a nearby willow tree. He made up his mind to rest a little and then continue on his way.

Leaning against the trunk of the willow tree, the peasant began to think of all the money he would make from the sale of the grapes, and what he would buy with it to take back to the village. He would buy chickens, flour to make bread, new hoes and plowshares to hoe and till his land, and, perhaps, if there was enough money left, a new pair of shoes and a pair of baggy pants. Dreaming of all these things he was going to buy, he grew happy and contented, his eyelids felt heavy, and sleep overcame him.

When he woke up he saw that the donkey had gone. He searched and searched for quite a long time, but there was no sign of it.

"I must have slept a long time," said the peasant to himself. "The donkey probably got restless and took the road back to the village to be with her little one again. Where else could she have gone?"

So he followed the road which he thought the donkey must have taken.

On the journey back, he met a traveler who was a peasant like himself.

"Fellow traveler," said the peasant to the man, "on my way to the market I lost my she-donkey. Maybe you came across her. If so, pray tell me, where was she?"

"Is your donkey blind in the right eye?" asked the man.

"Yes," said the peasant, "my donkey is blind in the right eye."

"Is one of her legs a bit shorter than the others?" added the man.

"Yes, yes!" replied the peasant, who by now was sure that the traveler had spotted his donkey.

"And was your donkey also carrying baskets of grapes?"

"Yes," answered the peasant. "My donkey was indeed carrying baskets of grapes."

To which the traveler said, "In that case, I regret to say I have not seen your donkey."

Having uttered these words, the traveler walked away, leaving the poor peasant rooted to the ground with astonishment. When the poor man had recovered his wits he ran after the fellow who had raised his hopes so high, only to dash them to the ground.

"I don't understand you," he said to him. "You tell me all there is to know about my donkey. You ask me if she is blind in the right eye, if one of her legs is shorter than the others, and if she is carrying baskets of grapes—and then you have the audacity to pretend that you have not clapped eyes upon her. You are lying, traveler, you are lying! You must have seen my donkey. Tell me where you saw her, and I'll let bygones be bygones."

"Don't be a fool," said the man. "I said I had not seen your donkey. I have nothing else to tell."

The peasant was certain that the traveler was lying, and refused to leave his side. Thus they both reached the market town, all the while arguing and throwing insults at each other.

When the peasant saw that he could not get the traveler to tell the truth, he became furious. He frothed at the mouth with rage, spitting fire. He marched off to see the local judge to obtain justice. The judge listened to the peasant's story, and ordered both him and the traveler to appear in court.

When the day of the trial came, the judge asked the traveler,

"Tell me this: This man here complains that you mentioned to him all sorts of details about his she-donkey, and yet when he asked you if you had seen her, you insisted on saying that you had not. What kind of story is this?"

"Yes, your Honor," replied the traveler. "I repeat it again: I have not seen the donkey belonging to this peasant."

"Well now, if you did not see her, how do you know that the donkey was blind in the right eye?"

"Sir, I could tell that by looking at the grass along the road. The donkey had only grazed the grass on the left side of the road. The grass on the right side was left untouched. That means that if the donkey's right eye had been sound, she would have seen and grazed the grass on both sides of the road, not simply on one side."

The judge was amazed, because what the traveler was saying made sense. The judge then said, "Very well, I accept that, because it sounds true. But how did you know the donkey had one leg a bit shorter than the others?"

"Very simple, Sir," retorted the traveler. "The road was very dry and dusty. I noticed that of the four hoofmarks left in the dust, three were quite clear, whereas the fourth was a bit blurred. I came to the conclusion that if the fourth leg had been as long as the other three, the fourth hoofmark would have been as distinct as the others. But it was not. It followed therefore that one leg was slightly shorter than the rest. Even a blind man could see that, Sir."

The judge lost his temper. "You are nothing but a cunning rascal. I admit that you were right about the eye and the leg of the donkey, but how did you know she was carrying grapes?"

"Sir Judge," answered the traveler, "being an observant man, I noticed that the donkey had grazed longer in places where the grass was more abundant. During this time, the grapes at the bottom of the baskets must have been squashed by the grapes lying on top of them. Under this pressure the juice must have oozed through the bottom of the baskets and dripped onto the grass. I could tell that by the swarms of flies buzzing around those spots."

38

The judge was so flabbergasted by this amazing tale that he came down from his rostrum and, heaving his very fat stomach, started dancing a jolly dance, in which he was shortly joined by the traveler. The peasant, smarting under the injustice of it all, watched them with anger in his eyes. But the dance was stronger than his wrath and the loss of his donkey and grapes, and soon he, too, gave way to merriment, and they all joined in a threesome reel, to the delight of the onlookers.

The Merchant's Son and the Slave

There was once a rich merchant of Jerusalem who had an only son. This merchant often traveled abroad on business affairs accompanied by his servant, while his son stayed at home busy with his studies.

Now it happened one day, during one of his journeys abroad, that the merchant fell ill, and soon realized that his end was not far off. He was very troubled, however, about making a will. He thought that if he made a will leaving all his money and possessions to his son, who was far away from

40

his father, the slave might take everything, run away, and leave the son destitute.

The dying merchant thought the matter over for a while. Then he called his servant and ordered him to call a scribe— a man practiced in drawing up wills and testaments. The scribe was instructed to draw up a will in which the merchant's son was enjoined to take the one object which he liked best, while the rest of the money and property was to be taken by the slave. After the merchant's death the slave returned to Jerusalem, taking the will with him. In due course he inherited the possessions of his late master.

When the son learned of his father's death he at once claimed, as his father's son and heir, his inheritance; but the slave refused to give it up.

"Look," said the slave, showing the young man his father's will. "Here is your father's testament by which everything is left to me, with the exception of one object which you are permitted to take."

The son, in his dilemma, decided to consult a certain rabbi famed for his great wisdom and skill in solving knotty problems. He related to this wise man all that had happened, and asked him what he should do.

"Do not worry, my son," said the rabbi, "for all will be well. Your father was a wise and far-sighted man. When he made this will he did you a great service. Now tomorrow morning come with me to the Court of Justice; let the slave also come with your father's testament; and follow the advice that I shall give you."

The following morning both the son and the slave appeared before the judge, and the will was read out for all to hear. When the merchant's son was asked by the judge what thing he claimed as his own, in accordance with the terms of the will, he pointed to his late father's slave and, following the advice given him by the rabbi, said, "I claim this slave."

He thereupon took possession of the slave and thus became master of all that the slave possessed: and in this manner came into his father's inheritance.

The Ape and the Two Cats

Two cats one day stole a piece of cheese from some mice. Since neither trusted the other to divide it equally, they took it to the ape and asked him to break it into two equal portions. The ape cut the cheese into two, but one part was larger than the other, so he bit a piece out of the bigger half to make it the same size as the smaller. But he bit off a larger piece than was necessary. Seeing that the two halves were still unequal, the ape took another bite at the larger of the two pieces, but with the same result. He repeated this process until the cheese was almost gone. The two cats, seeing that their precious cheese was gradually disappearing, told the ape to stop and let them have their cheese back.

"We are quite content with this division," they said, "so give us back our cheese and let us depart in peace."

"No," said the ape, "if you are content with the division, Justice is not content." And so saying, he went on gnawing at the two pieces of cheese in turn until he had finished the lot.

The two cats, sadder and wiser animals, walked away, saying, "There is no power save that of God above us, and no wrongdoer who is not afflicted by a greater wrongdoer."

A Lie for a Lie

There was once a governor of a Persian province who was known far and wide for his meanness and greed. One day, whilst he was in the council chamber busy counting his money, an itinerant poet appeared before him and started to recite some verses in praise of the Governor. When the poet had finished his eulogy the Governor applauded him, and complimented him highly on his fine poem. He then ordered his secretary to go and get the poet ten thousand *dirhems* from the treasury as a reward. On hearing this, the poor poet almost leaped into the air, so great was his joy. When the Governor saw how pleased he was, he said,

"No. I think you deserve more than that; it is a very fine poem. I shall pay you twenty thousand *dirhems* instead."

The poet could hardly believe his ears at that. The Governor, turning to his secretary, said, "I see that our friend's joy grows greater with every word I utter. Let us, therefore, increase his reward. Go and get him forty thousand *dirhems.*"

By now the poet thought that he must be dreaming. Shaking himself to make sure that he really was awake, he said to the Governor,

"You, Sire—may your life be long!—are indeed a generous and noble man. In all my born days I have never come upon anybody so openhanded."

With these words the poet once more wished the Governor long life, and respectfully withdrew from the council chamber into an anteroom. There he waited, hoping soon to receive the promised reward.

After the poet had left them, the secretary expressed surprise and astonishment at the Governor's generosity. "Sire!" he said. "That man would have been satisfied with forty *dirhems,* and yet you want to give him forty thousand."

"Don't be so stupid!" retorted the Governor. "This wandering poet gave us pleasure with mere words; so we, in our turn, gave him more pleasure with more words. When he praised me and said that I was more beautiful than the full moon, and stronger than the lion; that my tongue was

44

sharper than a sword, and my glance more penetrating than a lance, did he put into my hand anything substantial that could be rewarded with something equally substantial? No, of course not. We know that he was only lying. But his lies gave us pleasure. We, on our part, made him happy with our words, and promised him a reward in spite of his lies. Thus, in the end, it will be a lie for a lie, and words for words. For fine words are all the poet will get out of me in exchange for his fine words."

Having thus spoken, the Governor went back to counting his money, and the secretary returned to his duties. The poor poet, realizing that he was going to get nothing from the miserly Governor, went on his way, pondering on the ingratitude of people.

The Beardless, the Lame, and the One-Eyed Thief

There was once a merchant of Yerevan. When he lay dying, he summoned his son and said, "My son, trade anywhere you wish, but vow to me that you will not go to Aleppo to trade."

The father died, and they buried him; his son loaded his goods on his mules and began to trade in many towns. One day he came home, and said to his mother, "Mother, I am going to Aleppo on business."

His mother said, "Son, your father made you vow never to go to Aleppo."

Her son replied that there was nothing for it, he had to go. He made inquiries about what wares fetched a good price in Aleppo, and everyone told him that boxwood was very expensive there. He therefore loaded forty donkeys with this wood, said a prayer, and set off for Aleppo.

And so he journeyed, whether much or little God alone knows, until he came toward evening within sight of Aleppo. Outside the town there was an inn, and the servants came out and told him that the inns in the city would be shut.

"Unload your donkeys, spend the night here, and start out again for Aleppo early tomorrow morning," they said.

When they had unloaded the merchant's donkeys, the lame thief came and saw that his entire stock consisted of boxwood; he stole one bale, filled the hearth with half of the wood and threw the rest under the table.

When the merchants came together to dine, the lame thief asked the merchant from Yerevan what he had come to sell, and when he was told, he pointed to the boxwood lying all about the place and said, "We use that wood here for firewood, my poor fellow; it's like sending salt to Koghb. Never mind, I'll give you these seven bowls of gold for your wood, so that you may cover your loss."

The young man thought, and said to himself, "If I take this gold and return home immediately, they will ask me what I saw in the city of Aleppo, and what shall I say? I'll go first to Aleppo."

So next morning he entered the city of Aleppo, and turned this way and that in search of someone he might question on what he wanted to know. Finally he saw an old man in a shop, and he went in.

"Greetings, friend," he said.

"Greetings, a thousand greetings, stranger," said the old shopkeeper. "Where are you from?"

"From the village of Parp, near Yerevan," said the young man.

"What business brings you to Aleppo?"

"I have come to look around," said the young man. "Tell me: would you have any boxwood?"

"How much would you want?"

"Half a hundredweight, or a hundredweight perhaps."

"Goodness, brother, we do not sell it by the hundred-weight here. In the whole town there will be only four or five pounds, and an ounce costs thirty shillings!"

"Alas!" lamented the young man. "God is on high, you are down here. Help me." And he told the old shopkeeper exactly what had happened, and how he had been cheated. When he had finished the old man said, "My son, this is a tricky business. There are three thieves in league with each other, who cheat those who fall into their clutches. As to who might help you, the cook is the only man who can; go and ask him for advice."

So the young man returned to the inn, went into the

kitchen, and asked the cook to help him.

"Get me out of this predicament," he said, "and I shall reward you well."

"I shall work on your behalf," said the cook. "I'll tell you something that will certainly help you. When you go to your bedroom this evening, make a hole in the wall, and put your ear to it. The three thieves—one is beardless, one lame, and one one-eyed—will come and ask questions of Ne'er-say-good; when you hear what advice he gives them, act upon it."

The young man did as the cook said, and soon found himself listening to the conference of thieves.

"Ne'er-say-good," said the three thieves, "a merchant from Yerevan has brought forty bales of boxwood, for which we have offered him seven bowls of gold. How much will the forty bales bring us in?"

Ne'er-say-good said, "He's a Yerevan man, who has been everywhere. You know many tricks, but he knows seven times as many. Supposing he says, 'I do not want gold, give me seven bowls of fleas,' what will you do?"

"May thy house prosper, Ne'er-say-good," said the thieves. "He'll never think of that."

But he did. The merchant had heard everything, and the next morning he went to the landlord of the caravanserai, and asked him to summon the three thieves so that they might settle the price of his forty bales of boxwood, and he might go home.

The landlord summoned the thieves and bade them pay the merchant.

48

"We owe him seven bowls of gold for them," they said.

But the merchant said, "I have many farms and have no need of gold. My herdsmen are always sleeping, and my sheep and cattle get hurt. Instead of seven bowls of gold, I want seven bowls of fleas to keep them awake, four bowls of females, three bowls of males."

There was nothing for it. The thieves went off to Aparan to collect fleas. As soon as they caught one, and were wondering whether it was male or female, it jumped away. Seeing that they could not fulfill the contract, they returned to the inn. When the merchant had gone to inspect his wares, they found a man whom they bribed with a hundred rubles and a roll of linen.

"Wherever that Yereven merchant goes," they said, "you go with him; when you know all about him, come back and tell us."

This the man did. He introduced himself to the merchant and became his drinking companion. It was not long before the young man, taking the other to be his friend, had told him all about himself, where he was from, who his father was, and so on. Then the man went and related everything to the three thieves.

The next day the merchant met the one-eyed thief in the street.

"Good morning, Martiros," said the one-eyed man. "How are your father and mother; how is so-and-so, how is this one, how is that one?"

The young merchant, somewhat surprised, stopped in his tracks.

"God be praised," continued the one-eyed thief. "I have been looking for you, and now I have found you. Many years ago when you were born, you had only one eye; I took one of mine out, and gave it to you."

Then the thief ran off to the magistrate, and said, "When the merchant Martiros was born, he had only one eye, and I took out one of mine and gave it to him. He has kept it ever since. But now I am old and weak, and need it. I beg you to recover my eye from him and restore it to me."

The magistrate summoned the merchant, and asked him if he knew the one-eyed man.

"Apparently he lived in our house once," replied the merchant, "but I do not recognize him."

"He says that one of your eyes belongs to him," said the magistrate. "And now he wants it back."

The merchant asked for one day's grace, and went to see the old shopkeeper in Aleppo, whom he asked for help.

"If anyone can help, it will be the cook," said the shopkeeper.

So he went again to see the cook, and asked him for advice.

"Listen again tonight at the hole in your bedroom wall," said the cook. "The lame, the beardless, and the one-eyed thief will consult Ne'er-say-good. Act on what he tells them."

That night the three thieves again consulted Ne'er-say-good and told him of the trick the one-eyed thief had played upon the merchant.

"Now let us see how he will get out of that, then," said the one-eyed thief.

But Ne'er-say-good said, "He is from Yerevan. You cannot get the better of him."

"But what can he do? Now that he knows they are going to put one of his eyes out, he will flee and leave his wares behind him."

"There is one thing he could do," said Ne'er-say-good, and told them, and, unbeknown to him, the merchant.

The next day, again confronted with the one-eyed man, the merchant said to the magistrate, "Very well, I am prepared for you to take one of my eyes out; but to prove that it really belongs to this man, you must take his out also, so that they can be weighed together; if mine weighs the same as his, then give it to him."

When he heard this, the one-eyed thief dashed out of the room, called his fellow thieves, the lame one, and the beardless one, and off they ran as fast as their legs would take them. Even today, if they hear someone breathe the name of Yerevan, they make themselves very scarce.

So, giving one bale of boxwood to the cook for his excellent advice, the merchant took his wares to Aleppo and sold them for a fair sum of gold, and then returned to his native land of Armenia.

And as their wishes came true, may your wishes also.

Three apples fell from heaven, one for the storyteller, one for his listener, and one for him who lends an ear.

The King Who Tried to Cheat Destiny

There was once a king who was very curious to know how his subjects lived and worked, what they talked about, and whether they were satisfied with their lot in life. He decided that the best way to find out was to go and mingle with them in disguise. So one day the king and the vizier—his chief minister—disguised themselves as merchants from a foreign land and went out into the city and the neighboring villages.

They spoke with all sorts of people, with other merchants, with shopkeepers, peasants, and many others. In their pose as strangers in the land, the two of them asked many questions about the country; whether its king was a just man or a tyrant, and whether the people were content with his rule. At the close of their first day they arrived at the poor dwelling of a peasant. He invited them in and bade them be seated, and gave them a frugal meal for which they thanked him.

Now this peasant had a young child, a boy, about the same age as the king's daughter. While the king and the peasant were busy talking to each other the vizier was watching the boy, who was on his mother's lap, very closely. For he, the vizier, was able to foretell the future of any person merely by studying his face. And he read from the child's face that one day he would marry the king's daughter. Turning to the king, he told him in a low voice that the peasant child would one day be the king's son-in-law.

"Don't be a fool, vizier," said the king, "I would never allow such a thing to happen. This child, who will remain poor and humble all his life, can in no wise be the husband of a princess. Now listen, and I will show you how I am going to prevent this marriage."

He then turned to the peasant and asked him if the child was an only one.

"No, indeed, sir," replied the peasant. "He has three brothers."

"I," said the king, "have no children. I would like to buy the child. I would adopt him as my own and give him a good upbringing and education, and make him heir to my wealth and property. Since you already have three sons beside him, would you not sell this one to me?"

At first the peasant and his wife hesitated. Then they thought how their son would be brought up in the rich merchant's house and inherit his money and become rich and, one day, be able to keep his parents and brothers in luxury and ease. Finally, the peasant and his wife consented. Thereupon the king paid them a large sum of money, and in exchange received the child from the man and his wife. The king and the vizier then left.

They walked along for a while, the vizier carrying the child, until they came to a river.

"Now," said the king, "see how I am going to cheat destiny." With these words he snatched the boy from the vizier's arms and threw him into the river.

"No, Your Majesty," the vizier said, shaking his head,

"you cannot alter what fate has decreed. The boy will be rescued and he will wed your daughter at the appointed hour; it is ordained."

The king laughed at his minister and told him not to talk nonsense. Then they returned to the royal palace under cover of darkness.

Meanwhile the child was carried along by the current of the river until he reached the mouth of a stream which turned the water wheel of a flour mill. But his body got caught against the wheel, causing it to stop going around. When the wheel ceased to turn, the miller thought that a boulder had got jammed against it. He climbed to the top of the mill to find out, and saw a child in the stream down below. He rushed down and pulled the boy out of the water, and found that he was still alive. He carried the child to his wife, crying, "God has sent us this child. We must look after it well and bring it up as one of our own children."

The miller's wife was as pleased as her husband to have the child. They brought up the boy as one of their own children, making no distinction between him and them. When the boy grew older the miller sent him to school with the other children. The boy was unusually intelligent and quick-witted, and quickly learned what was taught him. When he left school he stayed at home and helped the miller with his work. But the miller felt that this kind of work was not good enough for so talented a youth as his adopted son, so he cast about for some means of finding a more suitable occupation for the boy.

Now it so happened one day that the king and the vizier

were out on a hunting expedition in the neighborhood of the mill. As the heat of the day approached they dismounted and rested in the shade of some trees not far away. When the miller heard that the royal party was in the neighborhood, he went out and invited the king and the vizier to rest awhile in his house.

When they entered the miller's house the first person the vizier saw was the boy whom the king had thrown into the river. Although the boy was now a grown youth, the vizier recognized him at once. He drew the king aside and said to him in a low voice, "This young man is the child you once threw into the river; see, how he has grown. He is the one who will marry your daughter, Sire."

The king was much troubled in mind at seeing the boy and hearing again his minister's prophecy. He addressed the miller. "Is this young man your son?" he asked.

"No, Your Majesty," replied his host.

The miller then related the whole story of how he had rescued the boy from the millstream and brought him up with his own children. He also told the king that he was anxious to find some occupation for the boy in keeping with his intelligence and ability.

"Do not be anxious about the young man's future," the king told the miller. "I shall put him in the royal palace and see that he gets a good post there."

The miller's gratitude and joy knew no bounds at the king's generosity. He kissed his hands and wished him many years' happiness and glory. The king then wrote a letter to the queen, saying, "When the youth who is the bearer of this letter presents himself before you, have him put to death immediately. This is a command." He signed the letter with his name, sealed it, and gave it to the young man. He told him to deliver the letter to the queen with his own hands, and that she would look after him and have him appointed to a position of trust in the palace.

The youth bade farewell to the miller's family, embraced them all and set off with the letter. After a long journey he arrived in the capital, where he made straight for the royal palace. As he was feeling tired after his journey and the day was growing hot, he decided to rest for a short while in the shadow cast by the high palace wall before going inside to see the queen. So he lay down on the ground and was soon fast asleep.

Now it so happened that the spot chosen by the youth in which to take a rest was directly beneath the window of the princess's room; and by chance, almost at the same moment, she looked out of the window and saw him stretched out in sleep. She looked at him for some minutes. What she saw was a young man of about her own age with a ruddy complexion and chestnut-colored hair. "I wonder who he is?" she said to herself. "How handsome he is and how strong he looks. I would gladly marry such a man!"

Finally, overcome by her curiosity, the princess crept quietly out of her room, down the stairs and out of the palace to where the young man lay sleeping. She caught sight of the letter beside him on the ground, and saw that it was written in her father's hand. She picked it up and opened it. Her brow grew dark with anger as she read her father's instructions to the queen, her mother. Making sure that none of the palace servants had seen her, she took the letter back to her room, got another sheet of paper and, carefully and skillfully copying her father's hand, wrote the following:

"When the youth who is the bearer of this letter presents himself before you, marry him at once to our daughter. This is a command." The princess then signed it with her father's name, sealed it with the royal seal, and addressed it to her mother as her father had done. She tore up the old letter, quickly ran down again to where the youth was still asleep, and placed the new letter near his hand.

A little later the boy awoke, much refreshed by his sleep. He rose to his feet, picked up the letter, and approached the grand entrance to the palace. He told a palace guard that he had been ordered by the king to deliver the message personally to the queen. The youth was taken to the queen's chamber where he gave her the letter. She was puzzled at first when she read what the king had written to her. Why should he be in such haste to marry their daughter, the princess, to an unknown youth? she asked herself. But it was a command, and the king must be obeyed.

The queen turned to the young man and spoke to him. She was impressed by his appearance and the way he spoke. He had a clear voice and his speech was pleasing to the ear. The queen then called the princess to her. "Are you willing to marry this young man?" she asked. "Yes, mother," answered the girl. And so they were married amid much rejoicing and ceremony.

A week later the king and his party returned from the hunt. As they entered the palace grounds the king saw his daughter walking along one of the paths with the youth whom he had ordered to be put to death. The monarch gazed at them in astonishment. Then he called one of his courtiers.

"Who is that young man?" he demanded.

"The princess's husband, Sire," was the answer.

In a rage the king went straight to the queen's apartment.

"What is the meaning of this?" he shouted angrily. "How comes our daughter to be married to this man? Did I not send you a letter ordering him to be killed?"

For an answer the queen showed her husband the letter the youth had given to her. The king took it from her hand and read it carefully. He could not understand what had happened. This was not what he had written; yet the handwriting and signature seemed to be his. He turned to the vizier and showed him the letter. The vizier smiled.

"Did I not tell you," he said triumphantly, "that you cannot alter what fate has decreed?"

The king accepted the situation with good grace, and appointed his son-in-law to an office of high rank at the royal court.

Maimonides and the Bottle of Poison

Moses Maimonides, or Moshé ben Maimon, as he is called in Hebrew, was a famous Spanish-Jewish philosopher who lived in the twelfth century. He was also a great doctor, and served at the Court of Saladdin in Egypt. Many legends have grown around the name of Maimonides the Physician. It is told that he had a dispensary in which there were shelves full of bottles of medicines. Whenever an ill person visited his dispensary for treatment, Maimonides would look at the medicine bottles, whereupon one of them would begin to shake; that very bottle was the one that contained the remedy.

One day a patient, after having visited all the other doctors in the town for a cure without success, went to Maimonides. The great physician listened to his visitor's complaints and then looked at the bottles. All at once a bottle of poison began to shake. Maimonides turned to the patient, saying, "I am sorry, but I have no cure for you."

He said this because he knew that if anything were to happen to the sick man through taking the poison, he, Maimonides, would be held responsible.

The patient went away, angry at receiving no remedy for his ills. He walked on for a long time until he came to a forest. There he lay down in the shade of a tree to rest awhile. He soon became parched with a burning thirst, and looked around for some water to drink. All at once he heard a dripping sound and saw drops of water falling into a jar from above. He rose to his feet, got hold of the jar, and took a drink of the water. After drinking it he at once felt that his illness had left him.

He went back to the town and told Maimonides what had happened. After hearing the patient's story Maimonides asked him to go back to the same place in the forest and find out where the water was falling from.

The man went back to the forest and saw on one of the branches of a tree a huge snake which was dripping poison from its mouth into a jar below. The man returned to Maimonides again, and told him what he had seen.

Maimonides then laughed, and said, "The bottle of poison that started to shake when you came to see me the first time was indeed the only remedy for you! But I feared that had I given it to you, the blame would have fallen on me, had you come to any harm."

The Clever Bride of Tunisia

Once upon a time in the Tunisian countryside there lived a peasant who was a widower, and his daughter. The girl was very beautiful and possessed of great wisdom.

One day the King of Tunisia, on one of his journeys through the country, passed by the village where the peasant and his daughter lived. On his way he passed cornfields ripe and ready for the harvest, and the village cemetery. Wishing to find out whether the villagers were wise or not, the king decided to ask the first villager he met some questions. It so happened that the first person he saw was the peasant. The king asked him two questions. The first one was whether he was going to use the corn after he had harvested it or not. The second question was whether the people buried in the village cemetery were dead or not.

The peasant could not understand the significance of these questions; in fact, he thought them rather silly. However, he was wise enough not to tell the king what he thought. Instead he begged the king to allow him a little time to think out the right answers.

The peasant went home and told his daughter that he had met the king; he also told her about the two questions. The wise girl at once realized the true significance of the king's questions. She told her father that the questions should not be taken literally. The first question, asking whether her father was going to use the corn after harvesting it, was put in order to find out if he had any debts which he would have to repay in corn; for if he had no debts he would use the corn for his own household. The second question was to discover whether the dead had been people of no account—and therefore forgotten by the living—or whether they had been good, and therefore lived on in people's memory. The peasant then went to see the king and gave him the answers to his questions. The king was very pleased with the answers and, as a reward, gave the peasant and his daughter a loaf of bread every day for two weeks.

One day, when the king was passing the peasant's house, he overheard the daughter telling her father that she was surprised that the king should reward them with loaves of bread; she could only suppose that the king was not really the son of a king, but a baker's son.

On hearing this the king became very agitated, and went at once to his mother and told her what he had heard.

"The peasant girl spoke only the truth," said the king's mother. "You are not the son of a king. Your father was a baker."

She then explained to him that she was unable to give the late king an heir to the throne. So when she heard that the baker's wife was expecting a child, she, the queen, asked her to give her the baby, should it be a boy. The baker's wife did as she was asked, and so an heir to the throne was provided.

The king was furious when he heard the story of his humble origins. He was afraid lest his subjects discover the truth and force him to abdicate. He therefore resolved to get rid of the peasant's daughter who had divined the truth of his low birth. Without delay, he ordered her to leave the country. No amount of pleading on her own or her father's part could persuade the king to change his mind. So with some food and water, and money she had saved, she set off on her journey, and eventually reached a beautiful city on the Mediterranean.

She decided to go no farther, but to settle down there. With the money she had taken with her, she opened a shop where she sold fruit and vegetables. She was a thrifty girl and saved a lot of money, and after a while she was able to buy a house for herself. But she was very lonely, and in the evenings she used to sit at her window and watch the people passing to and fro in the street outside her house.

One day the king of this city passed by her house and saw her at the window. So struck was he by her beauty that he at once asked her to marry him. She did not know what to say or what to do, for it was the custom in her country for the parents to choose a husband for their daughter and arrange the marriage; it was considered brazen for a girl to choose her own husband. But as the girl's father was far away in another land, she had to make her own choice; and she knew that she must therefore choose a man able to keep the marriage a secret, lest her father be shamed should the news ever reach his ears.

So that she could find out whether her future husband would be able to keep such a secret, the girl decided to put her royal suitor to the test. She thereupon told the king that though she would be willing to become his wife, she would first like to have a meal with him before making up her mind. So she invited him to a meal. She cooked a chicken for him, flavored with all kinds of spices and herbs. This he ate, leaving nothing but the bones. For dessert the peasant's daughter set before the king a watermelon which he devoured with great gusto. After such a fine meal he felt tired and sleepy and thought he would like a little rest to help his digestion. So he retired to the guest room and soon fell asleep. But so loud was his snoring that it could be heard all over the neighborhood. When he awoke, feeling much refreshed, he was told by the girl that she could not marry him. Puzzled and disappointed by her refusal, the king returned to the palace.

On arrival there, he summoned the grand vizier and asked him to go to the girl's house to try and find out why she had refused the king's offer of marriage. The vizier did as he was asked, and went to the girl's house. As soon as he set eyes on her he was so taken by her beauty that he forgot what the king had said and, instead, asked the girl to marry him. He was put to the same test as the king. He was given a tasty spiced chicken and a large juicy melon for his meal. He ate them with relish and then retired to the guest room where he soon fell asleep. His snoring was even louder than that of the king. When he woke up the girl told him that she could not marry him, giving no reason for her refusal.

The king was angry and disappointed at the failure of his minister to find out why the girl had refused the royal offer of marriage. Next he sent the young crown prince to the girl's house to ask her why she had rejected the king's proposal. Now the prince was an intelligent and astute young man, and he felt somehow that neither the king nor the vizier had understood the significance of the meal of chicken and watermelon. But he was determined to find out.

When the prince saw the girl he fell in love with her immediately and asked her to marry him, completely forgetting what the king had asked him to do. Instead of giving him an answer, the girl invited him to a meal, and gave him the same as she had given the king and the vizier— spiced chicken and watermelon. When the chicken was set before the prince, he cut it into pieces, shredded the pieces, and then threw it all away.

The peasant's daughter was very pleased at this, for it was clear that the prince had realized that the meal was a test. And she knew that he would be able to keep the marriage a secret, since when he cut up and shredded the chicken it signified that even if he were to be torn to pieces, as was the chicken, he would not give away the secret. Then the prince was offered a watermelon, but instead of eating it as the other two had done before him, the prince cut it into pieces and squeezed the juice out of it until it ran all over the table. By this action he signified that even if his blood were to be shed and made to flow like the juice of the melon, he would not reveal the secret.

After that they got married secretly and lived very happily, until the prince decided that he must go and see the king.

When the prince got to the palace the king asked him

where he had been and what he had been doing for so long. The prince, of course, refused to tell his father, as he could not reveal his secret marriage to the Tunisian girl. The king, in his rage at being disobeyed, threw the prince into prison, and warned him that if at the end of three months he had not revealed where he had been all that time, he would be executed.

Three months went by, but the prince kept silence. On the last day of his imprisonment he was taken out of his dungeon to the main square of the city to be executed. On being asked what his last wish was before being put to death, the prince begged to be taken to a certain quarter of the town (this was where he and his wife lived, but the king, of course, did not know that). The prince was granted his wish, and was led in procession, accompanied by mournful music and the shouts of the crowd. When his wife heard the music and the shouting, she looked out of her window to see what was happening. As soon as she saw the procession she knew that her husband was about to be put to death. Quickly she seized hold of a large bottle of scent, and flung it with all her might out of the window. It landed among the crowd and smashed into a thousand fragments.

This was a sign to her husband, the crown prince, that just as the fragrance of perfume spreads, so could the news of their secret marriage be spread abroad. The prince understood the sign, and at once broke the news to the people. In this way his life was saved. The king congratulated the prince on his marriage, and praised him for his fidelity and his wife for her wisdom and quickness of mind. All the populace celebrated the joyful event with feasting and merry-making, and the young couple lived in happiness and prosperity for many long years.

Badikan and Khan Boghu

There was and there wasn't (and there was no one good but God), there was a king who had forty sons. As soon as each boy came of age he sent him off to a distant land to perform feats of valor and to find a suitably pleasing girl to marry. By the time this story begins, thirty-nine of his sons were already married, but the Lord knows what feats of valor they performed, or whether they performed any at all. In any case, it was now the turn of the youngest son, whose name was Badikan. His father, the king, gave him a sword and bow and arrows, money and servants, set him on his charger, and with a "God prosper thy cause" sent him on his way.

Badikan traveled the length and breadth of many countries. He saw the kingdom of darkness, and the kingdom of light. Think of Agog-Magog, the demon Aznavor, man and beast—Badikan did battle with them all, overcame them, and passed on his way; but in the end not one of his retinue was left alive; his monies were all spent, and he was all alone when he came to a magnificent palace, such as has

68

not its like on earth. This palace had been built in the distant unremembered past, of huge solid blocks of iron and stone, and the strength of the ramparts completely beggar description. Badikan walked around and around the walls, peered in at the gate and windows, but saw neither woman nor maid, man nor beast.

"Lord God, what sort of place is this that I have come to?" he said.

He waited around until it grew dark, and suddenly he saw someone coming. It was a huge giant. His armor was of steel, his casque and shoes of bronze, his bow and arrows of wrought iron, and when he took a step forward the earth rumbled.

The giant stopped, sniffed the air, and said, "A man. There is the smell of a human being. I spend all day hunting in the mountains, and the prey comes knocking at my door. Where are you, who are you? Come forward, so that I can see you, or I'll crush you to dust between my hands!"

What could Badikan do? No arrow or sword would make an impression on that beast. He stepped forward into the presence of the giant.

"Who are you," asked the giant, "to dare to enter this terrain? Have you not heard the name of Khan Boghu?"

"I have heard of you," replied Badikan, "and that is why I came to see you. My name is Badikan, and I have traveled all over the world. I have fought and defeated demons and dragons, and now I have come to fight and defeat Khan Boghu."

69

Khan Boghu looked Badikan in the face and snorted, and Badikan picked himself up a mile away.

"Come on, Badikan!" called the giant. "You're a brave fellow. If you wish I'll keep you on; bring your sword and bow and arrows and serve me; they won't do me any harm and may be useful for hunting."

Badikan gave his assent, and began to dwell with the giant in his palace.

One day Khan Boghu said to Badikan, "You will have observed that I cannot suffer pain or death, but nevertheless there is pain in my heart. The King of the East has a daughter who has no like on earth. Seven times I have tried to carry her off, but have never succeeded. If you bring her back, say what you want and you shall have it. Here is a horse, money, and weapons. Take whatever you want and go."

Badikan gave his promise to return, and off he went to the city where the girl lived. He dressed himself in the local garb, learned the local dialect and, finding employment with a gardener, began to work in the vicinity of the king's palace. One day the king's daughter looked out of her window and saw that when Badikan was left alone he would put on the most magnificent robes and parade proudly up and down, obviously a much grander person than a common gardener.

Well, the princess lost her heart to Badikan, and began to dream of him; and Badikan fell in love with her.

The girl did not hesitate long, and soon sent one of her

maids to declare her love to Badikan, who in turn told her that he was the son of a king, that he had performed many brave exploits, and that her fame had brought him thither. Having seen her, he had fallen in love with her and awaited her command.

Now the city was heavily fortified, and the inhabitants, both male and female, strong and warlike, since they daily expected an attack from Khan Boghu. Therefore the princess arranged to come outside the city to disport herself on the banks of the lake, whence Badikan, "if he were a man, might carry her off."

So the princess left the city with a retinue of forty handmaidens. Badikan swooped down on horseback, swift and light as a fairy, caught the princess up onto the saddle behind him, and soared away like an eagle. Those left behind just stared, openmouthed, until they came to their senses and ran into the city to tell the news to the king. The king and all his citizens leaped on their horses and galloped after Badikan. By this time Badikan had hidden the princess behind a platan tree, and went back on his tracks to meet his pursuers. When they arrived he slaughtered and massacred them all, until the battlefield was covered with corpses, one on top of the other. Then he returned, swept the girl onto his horse and spurred it forward; they came to the sea, swam on the back of the horse to the other shore, and saw in the distance the garden house and seraglio where Khan Boghu dwelt.

"Badikan, may I die for your soul," said the maiden. "We

have ridden such a long way, and you have not spoken a word to show that you love me. Tell me the truth, for the love of God. Was it for yourself that you carried me away?"

"You have appealed to me in the name of God, so I must tell the truth," said Badikan. "I carried you away for Khan Boghu. I gave him my word."

"However much Khan Boghu had tried," cried the princess, "he could never have captured me, nor can you think that you would have succeeded either by cunning or sword, had I not wished it so. May all maidens walk in widow's black weeds, for they are the slaves of their heart. I came to be your wife, and if I cannot be, then I shall drown myself in the sea or dash myself against a rock, and become food for fishes or birds."

And many reproaches did she make to Badikan, and cursed men of stony heart and deceiving speech, and made ready to cast herself into the sea. Badikan's heart was touched, and he called upon God to witness that they would find a way to liberate themselves from Khan Boghu and marry.

Then Khan Boghu came to meet them, and expressed his gratitude to Badikan, and his joy at seeing her to his beloved princess, and commanded that she be carried to the garden house, treating her very gently lest she should be repelled by his appearance and do herself a fatal injury.

"Are you quite well? Tell me your heart's desire, that I may fulfill it," he said to the princess.

"Thank you, I am very well, and you shall be everything

to me," replied the maiden. "But my father and mother made me promise not to take a husband for seven years, otherwise they would curse me, and cut me off from the fruits of my father's labor and my mother's milk. Will you accept not to be my husband until the seven years are up?"

"Gladly," said Khan Boghu. "Since you are in my hands, I should be patient not for seven years, but for forty-seven."

So they struck this bargain, and decided that Badikan should remain with them and should hold the crowns above their heads as best man at their wedding.

For some time all abided by this arrangement, but the princess and Badikan were not at ease. If they wanted to kill Khan Boghu, sword and arrow would not touch him; if they fled he would overtake them, and they would not escape his vengeance.

One day Khan Boghu rested his head on the princess's lap, and talked with her, and she with him.

"Why do you live all alone?" said the girl. "And how do you manage to survive when so many arrows and sword strokes rain upon you? Where is your soul? If you will not tell me this, I know you do not love me; and if you do not love me, say so, and I have no reason to live on."

She said many other things, and so cunningly, that Khan Boghu was persuaded to tell her his secret.

"Seven days' journey from my palace," he said, "there is a white mountain; in this mountain dwells a white ox, completely indomitable, for neither man nor beast can approach him. For seven days he goes without drinking, and on the seventh day he mounts to the summit of the white mountain. There, there is a spring of white water flowing through seven spouts of white marble. The white ox drinks from each of the seven white spouts, and then withdraws for seven days. In the belly of the white ox there dwells a white fox, and in the belly of the white fox there is a box of mother-of-pearl. In this box there are seven white sparrows. They are my soul, my seven secret powers. The white ox cannot be overcome, the white fox cannot be caught, the white box will not open, and the white sparrows no hand can seize. And therefore it is that I remain invulnerable, unconquerable and immortal, for if the ox is slaughtered, the fox runs off; if the fox is caught, the box will not open; if the box is opened, the sparrows fly away."

It was not long before the princess related Khan Boghu's secret to Badikan, saying, "If you are a man, do what you have to do. I have done my part."

A few days later, Badikan asked Khan Boghu to let him have the fire horse, so that he might travel to distant places and then return. Khan Boghu gave his permission, and Badikan set off. He went straight to the dervishes and sorcerers, and asked them, "How may an invulnerable man, whom fire and iron will not harm, be overcome; and how may an indomitable animal be tamed?"

The dervishes and sorcerers answered and said, "A strong man is overcome by woman, a wild beast by wine."

Badikan loaded a mule with seven barrels of seven-year-old wine, took them to the white mountain, and emptied them into the spring. The white ox came to the spring, smelled the wine, jumped higher than seven poplar trees, and galloped away roaring. The second day he came again parched with thirst. What could he do but drink the wine, get drunk, stagger back to his lair and fall asleep? Badikan followed him, drew his sword, and cut off his head.

At that moment Khan Boghu was out hunting; as the ox's head fell, his own head began to throb, and his whole body trembled.

"Akh!" he cried. "The white ox is dead. The princess has told my secret to Badikan or to some other suitor. I am dying, but I shall kill her first. If I cannot have her, no one shall."

He ran furiously into the palace.

By this time Badikan had cut open the ox's belly, and seized the fox by the tail before it had a chance to flee. He cut off the fox's head, and blood began to flow from Khan Boghu's nose. Badikan found the box of mother-of-pearl, and broke open the lock; Khan Boghu tasted blood in his mouth, but he hastened on to the garden house. The princess was terror-stricken and ran up onto the roof, determined that the giant should not take her alive; she would throw herself from the roof first.

Badikan strangled two of the white sparrows, and Khan Boghu collapsed at the knees.

Badikan strangled two more white sparrows, and Khan Boghu's arms grew numb.

Badikan strangled yet two more sparrows, and Khan Boghu's heart burst.

Badikan strangled the seventh sparrow. A black smoke

issued forth from Khan Boghu's mouth and nostrils, and he fell flat on the ground and lay still.

Badikan galloped back on the fire horse, the princess came down from the roof of the garden house, and they embraced and congratulated each other. And submitting to the will of God, they married, and lived happily ever after.

The Covetous Minister

In the city of Cordoba, in southern Spain, there once lived a merchant called Yusef. He was known throughout the town for his honesty and uprightness in his business dealings, and he had never broken a promise.

One day a man came to Yusef with a necklace of precious stones and asked him to sell it on his behalf for five hundred gold dinars. It so happened that when the merchant was carrying the necklace with him on his way to a buyer, he met one of the ministers from the court of the Emir, the ruler, of Cordoba. Now this minister was an avaricious man who coveted the property of other people, so when he saw the precious necklace in Yusef's hand, he wanted to know where he had got it from and what he was going to do with it.

"Your Excellency," said Yusef, "this necklace has been entrusted to me by a certain person for sale, and I am to sell it for five hundred gold dinars."

"Would you sell it to me for four hundred dinars?" asked the covetous minister.

"No," replied Yusef, "the owner wants five hundred gold dinars for it, and I promised him I would not sell it for less."

The minister, anxious to get possession of the necklace, then said to the merchant, "Come along with me to my house so that I may show the necklace to my wife, and, should she like it, I will buy it from you and pay you the price asked for it."

The honest merchant, suspecting no trick, followed the minister to his house. When they reached the door, the minister took the necklace from Yusef and, telling him to wait a minute or two, went into the house and shut the door, leaving Yusef standing outside. A long time passed, but the door remained closed, and there was no response to the merchant's repeated knocking and calling. In the end he went home with a heavy heart. He could hardly sleep that night for thinking about the necklace, and what its owner would say when he learned what had happened.

Next morning Yusef went around to the house of the minister, and found him on the point of leaving for the palace.

"Your Excellency," he cried, "do you wish to buy the necklace, or shall I take it back and sell it to some other person?"

"I do not know what necklace you are talking about," replied the minister haughtily.

"It is the necklace that you took from me yesterday to show to your wife," said the merchant.

"What talk is this?" the minister shouted. "You are mad! Go, before I punish you for your insolence."

Fearing the minister's wrath, and realizing that he could not get the necklace back from him, Yusef went to the Court of Justice and laid his case before the judge, telling him all that had happened. How, he asked, could he go back to the man who had entrusted the necklace to him and tell him that he had lost it?

Now the judge knew Yusef well, and could see that he was telling the truth; he also knew the minister for an avaricious and unscrupulous man.

"Be of good courage, Yusef," said the judge. "I will help you to get the necklace back."

The following morning the judge invited all the nobles and wise men of Cordoba to attend his court; this was his custom when he wanted to consult them on some matter of importance. Before their arrival he called his servant to him and said, "When a certain minister of the Emir comes—and I will point him out to you—wait until he has taken off his shoes and left them in the vestibule of the court. Then take one of the shoes and go with all haste to his house. Ask his wife to let you have the necklace which her husband brought home yesterday, because he is very anxious to show it off to his friends and let them admire it. When she asks you for proof of your words, show her the shoe and say that the minister gave it to you."

The servant did as the judge bade him. He went to the minister's house, and the wife, seeing her husband's shoe, did not suspect anything and handed over the necklace. The servant then hurried back to his master. At the same time he returned the minister's shoe to its place in the vestibule.

When all the nobles and wise men had left the Court of Justice, the judge asked his servant whether he had brought the necklace. When the servant produced it, the judge sent for the merchant.

"Here is your necklace," he said. "It was taken from you by a trick, and by a trick we have got it back from the thief."

When Yusef saw the necklace, he rejoiced and kissed the hands of the clever judge who had so wisely seen where the truth lay.

Two Watermelon Stories

Once upon a time, when the monkey was hairdresser and the hen watchmaker, when the sheep was beadle and the blackbird coal merchant, there lived a little boy. One day, after playing in the village square with his playmates, he began to feel hungry and so went running home. When he reached the house where his parents lived, he was told that his father had just been born, and an egg was placed in his lap. The boy was so astonished that he dropped the egg. Out of the egg came an enormous rooster which ran into the street.

The boy chased the bird, and threw a stone at it but missed. Then he threw a walnut, but the walnut grew into a giant walnut tree. The boy started to throw stones at the tree, trying to knock down some nuts, but missed them every time. So he decided to fling a handful of earth. This landed on top of the tree and became a field. The villagers gathered around the boy. Some told him to sow wheat in the field, some said it would be better to sow watermelons. The boy planted watermelons because he liked them very much. The melons which grew in this field were so big that even camels could not bear them away.

One day a man came and asked the boy to let him have a taste of his fruit. The boy gave him a watermelon. The man ate, and ate, and ate, but he couldn't manage to get through even one half of the fruit. Seeing that, the boy himself wanted to cut open a watermelon. As he was cutting it his knife slipped inside. He put his hand into the watermelon, but could not find the knife. He put his eyes inside, but could not see the knife. In the end, he himself went in. For seven whole years he walked and searched, but still there was no trace of the knife. He walked straight, he walked crooked; he walked in circles and he walked in squares, until in the end he arrived at the door of the melon.

This was a very strange melon indeed. On one side of it were grasslands and hayricks, and on the other were dusty, parched wastelands. On one side were blacksmiths beating their iron, on the other were dyers making dyes in a thousand and one different colors. There were also nations warring with swords and guns. The boy cursed the whole thing because he could make neither head nor tail of it.

Now years later a thief was walking along a country lane. He was hungry and thirsty, but there seemed to be nothing growing that he could possibly eat; there was no brook where he could satisfy his thirst. He grew faint and weary, and at last he sat down by the side of the lane to sleep and so drown his desire to eat and drink.

He was just about to doze off when he heard footsteps, and three naked men appeared. Without so much as a word of greeting, the thief stole three pennies from the pocket of one of the naked men, and ran all the way to the market square. There he bought himself a watermelon, the like of which he had never seen before. He could neither move nor carry it. So enormous was it that he decided to consume it on the spot. He took out his knife and made a cut, but the knife fell into the watermelon. Trying to retrieve it, the thief plunged his hand inside the melon. This time his hand disappeared. Trying to get his knife and his hand back, he himself fell into the melon. As he was looking around, a man came and slapped him on the neck so hard that his head fell off and made for the market to buy onions and garlic. The thief started running after his head. After a long race he finally caught up with it.

"You are my head," said the thief. "Get back where you belong."

But the head said, "You are neither my owner nor my master, go away, go away!"

There was much noisy argument between the two, which could have lasted for seven years and seven days. Only one course was open to them. They would have to go and consult the judge, who would surely know what should be done.

So they went to the judge's house, but he was not at home.

"Where is he?" they asked.

The judge had climbed up the lentil tree, they were told, to gather lentils. So the thief and his head went to the lentil tree. They found the judge perched on one of the top branches. After they had listed their grievances, the judge spoke to them. The branch on which he sat was so high that they could hardly hear his voice. But this is what the judge said.

"Your case is a very important and a most unusual one. I must listen to both of you and write down what you say. For this I need forty reams of paper and forty quills. Go and bring them. You must also fetch a ladder with forty rungs so that I can get down this tree."

The thief and his head did as they were bid. They went to the market and came back with forty reams of paper and forty quills. Then, after a long search, they found a ladder with forty rungs, which they propped against the lentil tree. As the judge was descending, the ladder broke and he fell down and died.

As for the thief and his head, they were reunited.

If you want to know what happened afterward, go and find another judge and ask him to write the head and the tail of this story with forty quills on forty reams of paper.

Hani the Simple

There lived, in one of the villages of the Lebanon, a man called Hani, and his wife, Maryam. Hani was a very good-natured but simple-minded man; he was also very lazy. Maryam was an intelligent and energetic woman; she kept herself and her husband by going out to work as a servant in the houses of the rich. She continually urged Hani to go and find some work, too, but all in vain; he just smiled and did nothing.

One day Maryam fell ill and was not able to go out to

work. She became very cross with Hani, and told him that unless he bestirred himself and obtained some work, they would both have nothing to eat. She advised him to go to the village mayor and ask him for some job as a donkey driver, to do portering and go on errands for him and his family.

Hani took his wife's advice, got up early the next morning and went to the mayor's large house. Now the mayor knew all about Hani and his simple-mindedness, and how his wife supported him by going out to work. So he took pity on him and decided to help him. He lent Hani a gold dinar, which was a lot of money, and told him to go and buy a donkey. The mayor then told Hani that his job would be to go to Beirut every day with the donkey, buy there what was needed for the mayor's household, and carry it back on the donkey. Hani did as he was bidden. He bought a good strong donkey in the market at Beirut and started work with the mayor. At the end of every day he received his wage.

One day the mayor told Hani to go down to Beirut and purchase a large quantity of rice from a shop which Hani knew well. But Hani felt particularly lazy that day and did not want to go to Beirut. It occurred to him, however, that he could send his donkey alone to make the necessary purchase and so save himself the trouble of going. But he first wanted to know if the donkey could go on its own and buy the rice. There was only one thing to do: to ask the donkey. So Hani loosed the animal's halter and put the question to it.

"Look," he said, "could you go by yourself to our friend the shopkeeper in Beirut, and buy a sack of rice and take it up to the mayor's house?"

The donkey, as if in reply, moved its head up and down—a habit that donkeys have. But Hani thought that it had understood and was telling him that it would go. He was, of course, very pleased at the donkey's willingness. So he wrapped a length of cloth around the donkey's head, like a turban, and in its folds put a dinar which his master had given him to buy the rice. Hani then put the donkey on the road to Beirut and watched it trot off till it was out of sight. After that he went back home. His wife was surprised to see him at that hour of the day, and without his donkey. She asked him why he had not gone to Beirut, and what had become of the donkey.

"I sent the donkey on its own to Beirut," replied Hani. "I asked it first, though, if it could go by itself to Beirut and buy the rice and take it to my master, the mayor. The donkey said it could, and off it has gone."

"You idiot!" shouted Maryam in anger. "You brainless fool! Now you have lost the donkey and the dinar with it. Go back and find it. Hurry, there is no time to lose. And don't come back without the donkey or the rice."

Hani ran out of the house down the road to Beirut. He ran and ran till his tongue was hanging out from exhaustion; but there was no sign of the donkey. On reaching Beirut, Hani went straight to the rice merchant and asked him if the donkey had been in to buy some rice. The shopkeeper took one look at Hani and decided that he was not very bright, so he thought he would have a joke with him. Yes, said the shopkeeper, the donkey had been in that morning, but not being satisfied with the quality of the rice, the animal had gone to another shop which also sold rice. Hani went to this shop, but did not notice that the first shopkeeper had followed him, and was making signs to the second shopkeeper behind his back. This one quickly grasped the meaning of the signs and asked Hani what he could do for him. When Hani inquired about his donkey, the shopkeeper said, "Yes, Hani, your donkey came in some time ago; but not being satisfied with Beirut rice, it decided to go to Haifa to buy some."

Hani shook his head in perplexity. "There is only one thing to do," he said to himself. "I must go to Haifa and bring the donkey back, otherwise Maryam will throw me out of the house." So he borrowed a dinar from the shopkeeper, went down to the harbor, and boarded a sailing ship which was bound for Haifa.

On arrival at Haifa he disembarked, and wandered around the market places of the city in the hope that he might come upon his errant donkey. But it was nowhere to be seen. In the end Hani stopped a man in the street and asked to be directed to the shop of the biggest rice merchant in Haifa. The man obliged, and guided Hani to a large store. Hani entered and asked whether his donkey had been in to buy rice for his master. Now the owner of the store had a grudge against the chief cadi, the judge, of the city, and when he heard Hani's request he suddenly thought how he could pay the cadi back and make him look a fool. He turned to Hani and said in a friendly voice, "Yes; your donkey came into my store some time ago and began to argue with me over the price of the rice. Before long a large crowd had gathered around my shop to see what all the noise was about. They were so impressed by the donkey's intelligence and shrewdness in argument that they had it appointed as cadi. Your donkey is, at this very moment, giving judgment in the courthouse dressed as a man."

The store owner then led Hani to the court entrance and told him where he could find the cadi. But Hani was afraid that his donkey, in its grand new position as a judge, would refuse to go back to the village with him. So Hani went and bought a large bunch of fresh carrots and hurried back with them to the court. But when he tried to enter, a guard stopped him and told him roughly to go away. Hani protested angrily.

"Let me in!" he shouted. "Let me in! I must see my donkey. He is the cadi now in this court, and I have got to see him."

The cadi, hearing all the commotion outside his court, demanded to know what was going on. When he was told about Hani, he at once guessed that this was the work of his old enemy, the store owner. He controlled his anger and ordered the guard at the door to let Hani in. When Hani appeared he waved the bunch of carrots in front of the cadi, saying, "This is my donkey, wearing the robes of a cadi. I hid a gold dinar in its turban."

The cadi realized at once that Hani was rather simple,

87

and that the store owner had taken advantage of his simple-mindedness in order to get his own back on the cadi. He turned to Hani and addressed him kindly.

"How much did you pay for your donkey?" he asked.

"A gold dinar," replied Hani. Whereupon the cadi took four gold dinars from his pocket and handed them to Hani, saying, "Take this money and go back home."

Hani left the court, rejoicing, and pondering the strange ways of donkeys. He returned to Beirut and repaid the dinar which he had borrowed from his shopkeeper friend there. He then bought a new donkey and a sack of rice, and set off for the house of the mayor. After a while his hand began to chafe from holding the beast's halter, so he fixed it to the back of his belt and walked in front of the donkey. The pair of them went plodding up the mountain road while Hani, oblivious of his surroundings, hummed a song to himself, and so failed to notice the three young men who were following him.

The three youths knew all about poor Hani and wanted to play a trick on him. When they reached a bend in the road, one of them stealthily untied the donkey's halter and tied it around his own head. His two companions then quickly made off with the donkey and its load of rice. After a little while the youth with the halter stopped. Hani, feeling the rope pull tight, looked around to see why the donkey had stopped. He could hardly believe his eyes when he saw, not his donkey, but a young man.

"Who are you?" asked Hani.

"I am your donkey," came the reply. "I used to be a man like you. But one day I came home drunk and shouted at my mother and began breaking and smashing things, and in her anger she put a spell on me, and I was changed into a donkey. On the way up here I prayed to God and begged forgiveness, and promised never again to go home drunk and shout at my mother. And, lo and behold, my prayer was answered and now I have been changed back into a man. Now let me go; I must return home."

Hani shook his head in bewilderment. "But where is the sack of rice which was on your back?" he asked.

"Ah!" replied the youth. "When I became a man again the load fell off my back onto the road, and I do not know where it is now. Free me from the halter rope, and we'll go back and look for your rice. I hope the next donkey you get is better than me."

The two of them set off back down the road to Beirut. When they reached the town, the young man disappeared in the crowds, leaving Hani alone with neither donkey nor rice. With the remaining dinar Hani went to the donkey market to buy another beast.

Looking around the market Hani caught sight of his donkey for sale. The young men had, of course, sold it to the donkey dealer. Hani knew it was his old donkey by a small mark on its right ear. He went up to the owner.

"Excuse me," he said, "could I have a word with that donkey?"

The man looked at Hani and laughed. "Yes, brother, do

as you wish. Go and have a word with him if you like."

Hani put his mouth to the donkey's ear. "Look, you rascal," he said, "it is quite clear that you haven't really repented of your bad behavior to your poor old mother, and now you have been turned into a donkey again. I wouldn't have you back now even if you were given to me for nothing!"

So Hani bought himself another donkey, and was soon back at work again and going errands for his employer the mayor. With his wages he replaced the stolen rice, and repaid the dinar which he had borrowed from his master to buy his first donkey.

His wife Maryam had, in the meantime, recovered from her illness, and the two of them lived in comfort and ease for the rest of their days.

The Goldsmith, the Wood Carver, the Tailor, and the Hermit Who Quarreled Over a Wooden Woman

Once upon a time a goldsmith, a wood carver, a tailor, and a hermit were traveling together. One evening they came to a clearing in a forest and, being tired after a day's journey, decided to spend the night there and rest. Before settling

down to sleep, the four of them arranged that one of their number should stand guard over the other three while they were sleeping. So they divided the night into four watches. The wood carver was to take the first watch, the goldsmith the second, the tailor the third, and the hermit the fourth and final watch.

After a little while, the wood carver, who was very tired, decided that the only way to keep himself from dropping off to sleep was to find himself some work to do. Looking around he espied a fallen tree trunk. He got his tools out of a bag and set to work on the wood. Soon he had carved a life-size figure of a beautiful woman.

When his watch had finished, he lay down to sleep, and the goldsmith then took his turn on guard over his companions. When he saw the wooden image, he said to himself, "The wood carver has shown his art by carving this wooden figure. I shall now show my skill by making ornaments for its ears, neck, arms, and feet; they will add to its grace and beauty."

He then fashioned ornaments of various shapes and sizes and put them on the image.

After the goldsmith's watch was over, he roused the tailor, whose turn it was to stand guard, and laid himself down to sleep. When the tailor saw the wooden figure of a woman, he said to himself, "How handsome a figure it is, and how exquisite are the ornaments that adorn it. I must also show my skill to the others. I shall sew for it a garment fit for a bride, and thus add even more to its grace and beauty."

So saying, the tailor took needle and thread and cloth

from his bag, and sewed a fine gown which he put on the figure.

When the hermit's turn came to watch over his sleeping companions, he looked in wonder and amazement at the wooden image dressed up in fine clothes and bedecked with exquisitely wrought ornaments. He sat on the ground and, for a while, remained deep in meditation and prayer. Then he cried out, "O Creator! Breathe life into this image!"

Immediately the wooden figure came to life and spoke like a human being.

At sunrise the sleepers awoke, and when they beheld the woman before them, they fell in love with her, and each one of them wanted to marry her. Soon they began to quarrel and dispute among themselves as to which of them would marry her.

Said the wood carver, "I am the maker of this woman; I carved her with my own hands from the wood of a tree trunk. I, therefore, have the sole right to marry her."

"Nay," retorted the goldsmith, "on the contrary, she is rightly my bride. I, and I alone, fashioned these fine ornaments which now adorn her beauty."

"Surely only I have the right," argued the tailor, "to take this woman as my wife. Did I not make for her a gown fit for a bride?"

"You are all wrong," said the hermit. "This woman was no more than a figure of wood. But by the power of my prayer she became a living being. Only I have the right to wed her."

Whilst they were thus arguing as to which of them should

marry the woman, a wise man happened to pass by them. He stopped to inquire the cause of their dispute. They told him the whole story and asked him to judge between them. Then the man took a closer look at the woman, and exclaimed, "This is my lawful wife, and you four rascals have carried her off from my house."

He thereupon took the four men and the woman before a magistrate. On beholding the woman's face, the magistrate shouted, "This is my brother's wife whom he took with him on a journey. You have killed my brother and stolen his wife. You are under arrest."

With these words the magistrate had them escorted to the judge.

When the judge saw the woman, he said to the men, "Who are you and what are you doing with this woman? I have been inquiring about her for a very long time. She is a servant in my house, and she stole a lot of money from me and ran away, hoping to escape justice. Now where is my money? Answer me!"

By this time a large crowd of people had gathered to see what the altercation was about. Among them was an old man. After listening to the arguments on all sides, he said, "This is clearly a dispute that cannot be decided by any man. In a neighboring city there is a large tree of great age called the Tree of Decision. All disputes that men are unable to settle are taken to this tree. From it a voice comes forth, declaring on whose side there is right, and whose claim is false."

94

The seven men and the woman thereupon went to the tree to hear its decision. Each one of the seven men pleaded his case before the Tree of Decision. When they had all spoken, one after the other, the trunk of the great tree split asunder with a great rending sound, and the woman disappeared into the cleft, upon which the tree became whole again. Then from it a voice spoke, saying, "This woman belongs to none of you. She was created from the wood of a tree trunk, and to wood she has returned."

The King and the Two Owls

There once reigned a good and just king much loved by his subjects. When he died he was succeeded by his son. But the new king was not like his father; he neglected his duties and his people, and spent his time in pleasure and kept the company of evil people. He levied heavy taxes on the country and allowed all sorts of injustice and wrong to be committed in his name. Trade declined; the merchants and farmers became poorer and poorer, and soon the kingdom began to fall into ruin. This state of affairs saddened the chief minister, who remembered the prosperous days of the young king's father. But because of his respect for the memory of the old king the minister kept silent.

One day the king went out hunting, taking his chief minister with him. As they rode along they passed through wild and deserted countryside with abandoned farms and ruined houses. They met with no living creature, save a wild animal here and there; they heard no sounds save the jackal's howl in the distance, and the hooting of owls amid the ruins. As they passed one group of owls the minister gave a sudden laugh.

"What makes you laugh?" asked the king in some surprise.

"Nothing, Your Majesty," answered the minister.

"You must tell me what it is that made you laugh," insisted the king. "People do not laugh for nothing."

Said the minister, "I was laughing at something the owls said."

"Do you understand the language of birds, then?" asked the king.

"Yes, Sire," was the reply.

"Then tell me what the owls said," commanded the king.

"I cannot tell you, Sire."

"You must tell me," ordered the king, his voice rising in anger.

"Let it be so, then," said the minister. "I will obey Your Majesty's command, but you must pledge that no harm shall befall me."

"No harm shall befall you; I promise you," said the king.

"Well," went on the minister, "two owls were conversing with each other—a male and a female—and this is what they were saying. 'We must raise a family of owlets one of these days,' said the male owl. 'Where will we find enough ruined buildings for them to live in?' asked the female owl, his wife. 'Have no fear,' answered her mate. 'If the king of this land lives long enough, our children and our grandchildren will never lack ruins in which to dwell in comfort.'

"And that, O king of the age," concluded the minister, "is what I heard the owls say."

When the young king heard these words he at once understood their import, and he took them to heart. He made a vow there and then to abandon his dissolute way of life, and from then on devoted his energies to working for the good of his country and its citizens.

The Stupid Hunter and the Crafty Bird

A hunter once trapped a bird which was very wise and could speak seventy languages. Wishing to free itself from the snare, the bird said to the hunter, "If you set me free I will teach you three rules of life which will be of great use to you as long as you live."

"All right," said the hunter, "teach me these three rules and I will set you free immediately."

"Then give me your solemn word," returned the wily bird, "that you will keep your promise and let me go. Only then will I tell you."

Whereupon the hunter swore a solemn oath that he would keep his promise to the captive bird and free it from his net.

"Good," said the bird, "these are the three precepts. The first is: Never regret anything that has already happened. The second is: Never believe anything you are told that seems impossible and beyond belief. And my third precept is: Never try to get anything that is unattainable and beyond your power to reach."

Having spoken these words, the bird reminded the hunter of his promise and asked to be set free. The hunter thereupon opened his net, and the bird flew away onto the branch of a tree well above the man's head. It then called mockingly to its erstwhile captor below,

"What a stupid man you are! You have allowed me to get away from you. Do you not know that a pearl of great price is hidden in my body; a pearl that is the fount of all my great knowledge and wisdom?"

When the hunter heard these words he bitterly regretted having let the bird get away from him. He rushed at the tree and tried to climb it in an attempt to reach the branch on which the bird was sitting. But his efforts were in vain, and he fell to the ground, breaking one of his legs. The bird laughed aloud and cried,

98

"What a stupid man you are, to be sure! Barely a few minutes have passed since I taught you the three precepts to follow, yet you have forgotten them so soon. I told you never to regret something that is already past; yet you regretted having set me free. I told you never to believe anything that is clearly beyond belief; but you were foolish enough to believe me when I told you that I carried a costly pearl in my body. I am but a poor wild bird that has to hunt every hour of the day for a few scraps of food. And lastly, I advised you never to try to reach the unattainable. But you were foolish enough to try to catch a bird with your bare hands. For all your pains you have gained nothing save a broken leg."

And with these parting words, the wise bird flew away in search of its next meal.

The Three Apples

A long time ago, when the time that was, was the time that was not, there lived a king in a certain country. He was not, like so many others, greedy for might and power. No, this king was as noble as he was good. In his reign the people of his lands enjoyed such prosperity, and law and order were so willingly observed, that thieves and tricksters went out of business. Ogres no longer dared to eat people, and evil spirits no longer dared to cast their spells.

Life was good. People worked well and lived well. They never felt hungry or cold. Out of seeds came harvests and out of stones houses were made. Because they were free and loved their work and believed in it, everything these people did was real and true. Even their tilling was like making the earth come true. The gifts of their hands shaped the truth of their work. And the doors of their houses were as open as their hearts. Who would not have wished to live under a king who made all these things possible and be his faithful servant?

But in this radiant kingdom the only unhappy person was the king himself. The Almighty had given him the power to rule over vast countries, but the one thing that he desired most was denied him: the joy of having an heir who would take his place when the time came. The older the king grew, the deeper his sorrow became. Night and day he prayed to the Creator of the heavens and the earth but his prayers all went unanswered. It seemed as if the earth was made of iron and the heavens of steel.

One day, as the king was wandering in his palace, deep in dark thoughts which spread loneliness and despair in his heart, he came upon a man who had seen much of life and gained much wisdom in the course of his wanderings.

"O Sire," said this man to the king, "I can see that you are

100

distraught, but how can anyone help you if you never speak of the cause of your sorrow? A sorrow unshared finds no remedy. What has happened to you? What ill is it that afflicts you?"

To this the king sadly replied,

"Good friend, I thank you for your solicitude. There is great darkness in my heart. God has given me a mighty scepter to which many lands bow in allegiance, but what good is all this to me without a son? In the midst of my power I feel destitute. For seven years now I have been imploring the Almighty to brighten my life with the gift of a child, but He has turned a deaf ear to my entreaties. In truth, I think that He expects me to content myself with being a powerful king; but I ask you, would the greatness of His design be upset in any way if He were to grant me an heir?"

Hearing this, the man said, "O mighty one! It is not my place to give you counsel, but if a man feels and sees nothing else but his own sorrow, it will fester endlessly and blot out the sun and the stars. Perhaps you are lucky that you have no son. Perhaps it is your fate. For it would have been truly tragic for you if you had had a son and then lost him. What God giveth He taketh back unto Himself. You cannot lose what you have never had."

"You speak the truth," said the king. "But try as I may, I cannot shake off the sadness which weighs on my soul."

The wise man then said,

"Good king, there is a way out of every difficulty. You must master your sorrow before it gets the better of you. Order your gardener to plan for you the most beautiful garden ever conceived in this world. Let there be wonderful lakes in it, whose waters are rippled only by the gliding of graceful swans. This garden must be a haven for the happiest flowers, and its willows must never seem to weep. And let the nightingale there pour out its heart every day to the most beautiful roses. There you will feel at rest. You will be the nightingale and the rose, the flowers and the lakes. Being all this, you will have no time for pain or sorrow, and your heart will shine like the dew on the grass."

The king was very much taken by the picture thus drawn. He did as the man had counseled. He had his palace surrounded by the most beautiful gardens. The gardens of Queen Semiramis were no better than a mere pot of flowers in comparison with those that had been laid out for the king. But all these labors were in vain, for every time the king went down into his gardens, he found that his sorrow had got there before him. He found it waiting for him under every tree, in every blade of grass and every petal, until one day he could no longer bear this suffering. Everything in the gardens seemed to be his enemy. In a fit of madness he drew his sword and began to destroy the garden; he would have caused complete devastation had his wife not besought him to be calm.

She was aware of the king's sufferings, and many times she had secretly followed him into the gardens, and watched his attempts to find solace and forgetfulness there. She herself had become such a frequent visitor to the gardens that now she hardly left them. She spent most of her time looking after the trees and the flowers with all the unspent motherly love in her heart. If she espied a sickly bud she, too, would grow pale and worried. Every stick and stone in the garden came to know her footsteps. Growing things acquired the gift of speech to greet her. Plants told her of their healing powers. But the king's wife said there was no medicine which could save her from her sad fate.

"The king, my husband," she told them, "is sad because God has not seen fit to bestow on him an heir. I am sad because I have spent my married years sleeping next to an empty cradle. No, there is nothing you can do for me. It is not by taking herbs that I shall be able to achieve motherhood."

A big, half-withered tree standing nearby answered her with a sense of shame,

"Believe me, I know how distressed you are. Had I been as I used to be before, I would have borne an apple which would have answered all your wishes. But on the day when the king wrought havoc amongst us, I received so many wounds that there is no strength left in me. All I have left is a little offshoot at the bottom of my trunk. Use it as a cutting, plant it where the sun can see it, and one day it will give you the apple which I cannot offer you. But remember, you must eat one half of the apple, and the king must eat the other half."

The king's wife did as she was bid. She planted the cutting, and for seven years and seven days she nursed it and protected it from cold winds and scorching heat. In time the cutting grew into a full-size apple tree.

One spring morning, seeing the tree in full bloom, a tenderness stirred in her blood. Some months afterward, right on its topmost branch, the tree displayed a beautiful sun-blessed apple, redder than a pomegranate. The king's wife had the apple picked, cut it in two, ate one half, and gave the other to the king. And nine months, nine days, and nine hours later, she brought into the world a son as bright as the light of day.

The king was supremely happy. He ordered feasts to be given in every corner of his realm, and for forty days and forty nights the people made merry to celebrate the happy event.

Three apples fell from the sky, one into my mouth, one into the mouth of the storyteller, and one into the mouth of the child who listened to the story.

Master and Pupil

Once upon a time there was a poor peasant and his wife, who had an only son. One day the wife said to her husband,

"You must teach your son a trade. I should not want him to remain an unskilled laborer, such as you are!"

And she insisted so much that her husband had to give in. So he took his son, and they set off together in search of a master who would accept the boy as an apprentice to learn his trade.

On the way to town they came to a spring, and the peasant, who was very thirsty, fell on his knees and, putting his mouth to the jet of cool water, drank his fill. When he had drunk enough he wiped his mouth, lifted up his head and cried, "Ah, that's nice!"

Immediately out of the pool of water beneath the spring popped a devil's head.

"I'm Satzneisz," said the devil. "Who called me?"

"I did not call anyone," said the startled peasant. "I just said how nice the water was."

"It doesn't matter," said the devil. "Is there anything you want?"

The peasant told him that he was taking his son to apprentice him to a master to learn a trade.

"Do not look any further," said the devil. "Leave him with me, I'll teach him my trade. Come back in a year. If you recognize him, take him away; if you cannot recognize him, however, he belongs to me forever."

Now the devil had many such apprentices. Within the year he transformed them to such an extent that their parents could not recognize them, and they remained his servants forever. The peasant, of course, could not know this, and he left his son in the care of the devil and went back home.

A year passed, and the father came back for his son. As it happened, the devil was not at home. In the yard there were many young men of his son's age, but his son did not appear to be among them. The peasant began to despair.

"So that's it. I'll never recognize my son again," he thought.

Hereupon, however, one of the young men approached him, and said,

"Father, it is I. The master will be back in a moment, and he will turn us all into doves. When we fly off, I'll be in front, and when we fly back, I'll be the last. When the devil asks you if you recognize your son, point to me."

The master came back, and immediately turned all his pupils into doves; they flew off, wheeled around the sky, and then flew back.

"Well, which one is your son?" said the devil to the peasant.

The peasant pointed to the last dove to alight.

The devil was very angry, for he guessed that the son must have made an arrangement with his father during his absence; but there was nothing for it, the peasant had pointed out his son, and he had to be returned to him.

The peasant and his son walked away.

"What did the devil teach you in that year?" asked the father.

As he said this, the son jumped into a leafy bush. When he had disappeared inside, a golden egg came rolling out of the bush. The peasant chased after it, but could not catch it. His son came back out of the bush.

"You're not lucky at all," said his father. "While you were in the bush a golden egg came rolling past me, but I was too old to catch it, and it disappeared among the brambles."

As he said this, his son jumped back into the bush. Out of

the bush scrambled a golden hen. The peasant grabbed at it, but it darted away, and he lost it in the bushes. His son returned.

"No, we've no luck," said his father.

Suddenly he saw a golden hare scampering at his feet. He made a grab at it, but missed, and it ran into the bushes. His son came out of the bushes and stood before him.

"Whatever did the devil teach you, son!" exclaimed the peasant. "When there's gold running around on legs you're nowhere near, and when it's gone, there you are!"

His son laughed.

"Don't get angry, Father," he said. "The golden egg, the golden hen, and the golden hare were none but myself."

The old man was pleased to hear this, and they went on their way. Before very long they came to a field where a group of nobles were hunting hares. They were chasing one hare furiously, but their hounds could not catch up with it, and it disappeared into a thicket. The son said to his father,

"Go into the thicket and chase the hare out. I shall change myself into a hound and shall catch the hare under the very eyes of these nobles. They will approach you and ask you to sell me to them; don't haggle with them very long, but ask a high price, since they will give anything. Sell me to them and go on your way, and I shall choose my moment to join you."

This they did: the father went into the wood, chased out the hare, the son changed himself into a beagle, chased after the hare, and took him so skillfully that the nobles nearly went out of their minds with admiration. They ran up to the peasant.

"You must sell us that hound!" they cried.

The peasant first refused, and the price they offered mounted higher and higher. When it was very high indeed, he nodded his assent, took their money and gave them the dog. The nobles put it on a leash and led it away.

The hunting party raised another hare, and unleashed their newly acquired beagle. The hound chased the hare out of sight, far from the hunting party, then changed back into a young man and rejoined his father. They went on their way, as the hunters in the distance called in vain to their hound.

They had not gone far when they came to another group of nobles. These were falconers, but none of the falcons they loosed could catch the pheasant they were after. This time the young man changed into a falcon, flew up into the sky, plunged his talons into the pheasant, and brought it to the nobles who, wild with enthusiasm, ran up to the peasant insisting that he sell them his bird.

The peasant again drove a very hard bargain, took the money and went on his way. When the nobles released their newly-acquired falcon in pursuit of another pheasant, it flew out of sight, and changed back into the young man, who then rejoined his father.

As they continued their way homeward with the money, the son found that, although it was a fair sum, they had not really done as well as they might have, and he said to his father,

"I shall change into a horse; you will ride into town on my back and sell me for a high price. But make sure you do not

sell me to a man with speckled eyes, or, if you do, sell me
without the bridle, or you will ruin us."

No sooner said than done. The son changed himself into a
handsome charger, and his father sat on his back and rode
into town. Would-be purchasers crowded around the horse,
but they were all outbid by a man with speckled eyes, who
offered a heap of shining gold as tall as the horse itself. The
old man could refuse no longer, and he sold the horse to the
man with the speckled eyes. The latter reached for the bridle,
but the old man would not give it to him. The purchaser,
however, who was none other than the devil, protested loudly, "What does this mean? I give so much gold for the horse
and this man will not give me the bridle with it?" There
was nothing for it, the peasant had to give him the bridle.
The devil mounted the horse and rode away as though on
air, rejoicing that he had succeeded in getting back his pupil
so easily from the foolish old peasant. He came home, led
the horse into a stable and firmly bolted the door.

His pupil was very downcast, for he could see that there
was nobody to whom he could turn for help. The time passed,
and he could think of no way out. Suddenly, however, he
became aware of a tiny ray of sunshine that had penetrated
the darkness of the stable and, tracing its course, he discovered
that it came through a tiny hole in the stable wall. So he
turned himself into a mouse and slipped through. But his
master the devil had seen him; the devil turned himself into
a cat, and chased after the mouse. The mouse scampered
away with the cat in hot pursuit; the cat was almost upon it
when they came to a stream, whereupon the mouse changed

into a fish, and dived into the water. The devil changed into a net and cast himself over the fish, whereupon the fish changed into a pheasant and flew up high into the heavens. The net changed into a hawk; its talons were almost in the pheasant's flesh, when it changed into an apple, and fell down and down, straight into a basket the king was carrying. The devil right away changed himself into a knife in the king's hand. The king was just about to cut the apple in half, when it changed into a grain of corn. The devil turned into a hen, and began to peck at the corn on the ground. When it came to the last grain, this changed into a needle. Thereupon the devil turned into a thread, thrust himself through the eye of needle, and wound himself tightly around it. Suddenly the needle leaped into the fire; the needle jumped out again, but the thread was burned to ashes.

And so it was that the pupil got the better of his master. The needle changed back into a young man, and he went home to join his father and mother, and all lived happily ever after.

The Fowler, the Parrot, and the King

A fowler, who was hunting one day, came upon the nest of a parrot and her young. He quickly threw his net over them, imprisoning them all. The parrot, fearing for her brood, said to them,

"If you want to save your lives, the best thing for you to do is to pretend you are dead. The fowler, having no use for you, will then fling you out of his net and you will be free. If he carries me away, don't worry, for if I can prevent myself from being killed, I will manage somehow or other to get back to you."

The young parrots followed their mother's good advice, and pretended to be dead. The fowler, thinking that they really were dead, picked them up and threw them out of his net. At once they flew away and settled on the branch of a nearby tree, too high for the fowler to reach them. He, in a black rage at seeing how he had been so cleverly tricked, was about to kill the mother parrot, when she spoke.

"Why do you want to kill me?" she asked. "You will gain nothing by that. On the other hand, if you spare my life you will be able to sell me for a very large sum of money, and live in ease and comfort for the rest of your days. You see, I am a skilled physician, and knowledgeable in the arts of medicine and healing."

On hearing this from the parrot, the fowler was very pleased. He said to the quick-witted bird,

"Rai Kamrau, the king of my country, has for many years been afflicted with a grievous disease which no doctor has been able to cure. Would you, with your great knowledge of medicine, be able to cure our king?"

"What a stupid question!" replied the parrot scornfully.

"Of course I can cure him. Indeed, so great is my power as a physician and healer of the sick that I could cure ten thousand patients of any disease. Take me at once to this king of yours. Acquaint him with my skill and knowledge in the art of healing; then sell me to him for a high price."

So the fowler put the parrot in a cage and took her to King Kamrau.

"Mighty Kamrau," said the fowler, prostrating himself before the king. "I have brought with me a parrot from another country who is a skilled physician, and who can cure you of all your ills. I am prepared to sell her to the king of kings."

"You have done well to bring this parrot to me," said the king. "As you know, I am in need of a clever doctor. Tell me, fowler, how much do you ask for this wonderful bird?"

"Ten thousand dinars, Sire," was the reply.

At once the king paid the price demanded by the fowler, and dismissed him. The king then had a fine spacious cage made of gold for the parrot and ordered the choicest morsels for her to eat, and appointed a special attendant to look after her.

The next day, the parrot began her treatment of the king's disease, administering to him all sorts of medicines and drugs; she continued with the cure for many days. But all the while she was thinking hard of how she might escape from the royal palace and return to her little ones. It would be a difficult task, she knew. The parrot was closely guarded by the attendant during the daytime, and at night the cage was securely locked. She realized, too, that the king would not part with her. Not only had he paid the fowler a large sum of money for her, she was also a bird of unusual attainments. One morning, when the king was almost cured of his disease and was feeling very much better, the parrot suddenly thought of a way by which she could get free. Approaching the king, she said,

"Sire, you are now almost cured of the disease which has afflicted you for so long; but in order to complete the cure I must procure a certain medicine which cannot be obtained here. I beg you, mighty Kamrau, to let me out of this cage for a while, so that I may go and search for it."

The king, believing that the parrot spoke the truth, opened the cage door and set her free. She flew out at once from the palace, and was never seen again. For many a long day the king and his men searched for her, and he offered a large reward to anybody who could find and bring her back. But all in vain; for the parrot had gone back to her young ones, fulfilling the promise that she would return to them if she escaped alive.

Three Times Lucky

Faris was a lazy man, and not a very intelligent one at that. He did no work for a living but relied upon his wife to support

113

them both. She hired herself out to do people's washing and clean their houses for them. She managed to make just enough to support herself and Faris. One day, like other women who had husbands, Faris's wife told him that he had to go out and find work and earn some money. She suggested that he go to the royal palace and get a job there as a servant. At first, Faris took no notice of his wife, but in the end, tired of her constant nagging and scolding, he went out to look for work; any kind of a job was preferable to her continual nagging.

So one morning Faris set out for the palace. When he reached the gates of the palace garden he saw the king, accompanied by his attendants, feeding a flock of geese. Faris watched them from a short distance, hoping that one of the attendants would see him and get him a job in the royal household.

Now it was the habit of the king, when he fed his geese, to take off the signet ring, which he always wore, and place it on a large stone nearby. This he did as usual, and started to feed the birds with grain out of a bag. He failed to notice, however, that one of the geese had seized the ring in its beak and swallowed it. In fact, nobody saw what had happened save Faris, from where he was standing. When the king had finished feeding his geese he went to pick up the ring from the stone where he had left it. But it was gone; and it was nowhere to be found in the garden. The king was exceedingly angry, and threatened his servants that if the ring was not found he would execute every one of them. He gave them three days to find the ring, and if at the end of that period the ring was not found, he would carry out his threat.

When Faris saw the king's rage and heard him threatening the servants with death, he took to his heels and ran back home as fast as his legs would carry him, without telling anybody what he had seen. He burst into the house, trembling with fear. His wife, seeing him in this state, asked him what had happened. When she heard from him how the goose had swallowed the king's ring she stamped her foot in anger.

"You idiot!" she screamed at him. "You half-wit! Why didn't you tell the king or one of his attendants that you had seen the goose swallow the ring? You might have got a big reward, or been given a good job in the palace. Now, listen to me. Go back to the palace and announce in a loud voice that you can tell people's fortunes, and foretell the future, and reveal where things are hidden. The king will hear you and ask you to tell him where the lost ring is. Now, don't tell him straight away. Mutter incantations and strange words like magicians and conjurors do, and then reveal where the ring is."

Before sending Faris off to the palace, his wife hurried out and bought the kind of robe a magician might wear, and Faris put it on. He then made his way to the palace. When he got there he stood outside the palace gates and shouted in a loud voice what his wife had told him. The king heard the words Faris was shouting, and sent a palace guard to conduct him to the royal apartments. Faris bowed low in front of the king and greeted him humbly. The king returned his greeting, and said,

"I heard your cry outside the palace that you are skilled in revealing hidden things. I want you to find out how I lost my ring in the garden, and where it is now. If you succeed in finding it, I will reward you handsomely. If not, I will have you put to death as a charlatan and a trickster."

Poor Faris trembled with fright at these words, but managed to conceal his fear. He took the king's hand and studied his palm closely as if reading it. He then let go of the royal hand, and with his own hand made passes in the air, muttering to himself all the while as magicians do. Suddenly he looked the king straight in the face.

"Were you feeding birds at the time you lost the ring?" he asked.

"Yes," replied the king, in some astonishment.

"Would Your Majesty show me the birds then?" asked Faris.

In answer to his question, the king led Faris into the garden and paraded the geese before him. Faris scrutinized the geese carefully until he saw the one that had swallowed the king's signet ring. He knew it by the black ring around its neck. He seized it and, turning to the king, said, "The ring is in the crop of this bird."

"How can that be?" the king asked in wonder and surprise.

"This goose swallowed the ring," was Faris' reply. "Slaughter this bird, cut open its crop, and you will find there the lost ring."

"Good," said the king. "I shall have the bird slaughtered. If what you say is true, you shall be well rewarded. If not, I

116

will know that you are nothing but a liar and pretender, and you will suffer the wretched fate of the bird."

The king ordered the goose to be killed and its crop cut open. This was done and, behold, there among the grains of corn lay the missing ring! The king was overjoyed at its recovery. He praised Faris for his skill and gave him a reward of a hundred gold pounds.

Faris took the money home to his wife. She could hardly believe her eyes when she saw so much money. She at once went to the market where she bought food, new clothes, furniture for the house, and other things they needed.

Now, when the king paid Faris his reward, the grand vizier was present. In spite of his exalted position at the king's court, this minister was envious of Faris' luck. He did not believe that Faris had used hidden powers to discover where the ring was, and he told the king so.

"Sire," he said, "this man is a lying rogue. He must have seen the goose swallow the ring. I do not believe that he possesses power to reveal hidden things. Let us test him with another problem. If he succeeds in solving it, he shall be well rewarded. If he fails, then we will punish him for deceiving us."

The king agreed to the grand vizier's suggestion. He gave orders that a frog be placed in a pot, which would then be covered with a heavy piece of fabric so that nobody would know what was inside. The king's orders were carried out, and soldiers of the royal guard were sent to Faris' house to bring him to the king.

Now Faris used to call his wife *Dafda'ah,* which is the Arabic word for "frog." That was not her real name, but he always called her that because she sounded like a frog croaking whenever she scolded him—which was often. When the king's soldiers arrived at the couple's house and told Faris that the king wanted to see him at once, the poor man was so alarmed that he turned to his wife and cried out, "O Dafda'ah, it is all up with me!"

But she bade him be of good spirit, and told him to obey the king's command and trust in God; all would be well with him. So off he went with the soldiers.

On arrival at the palace, Faris was greeted by the king.

"Faris," he said, "you claim to be one who knows all secrets, and you say that you can reveal what is hidden. Tell us then, what is in this pot. If you succeed you shall be given a big reward; if you fail we will know that you are a liar and a trickster, and you will be beheaded."

Faris trembled like a leaf at the king's words. He thought of his wife at home, and in his anguish cried, "O Dafda'ah, what did I tell you?"

On hearing this, all those present in the king's audience room, who had been told beforehand what was in the pot, broke out into loud applause.

"Bravo, Faris!" they cried. "You have told correctly what it was in the pot."

When the cover was lifted off the pot, the frog leaped out. The king was delighted, and looked at the grand vizier in scorn. Then he gave Faris a hundred gold pounds and let him go home.

Faris returned home rejoicing at his luck and good fortune. He related to his wife all that had happened at the palace, and how, when he called out his wife's nickname, the king and his friends thought that he was calling out to the frog. His wife could hardly stop laughing when she heard the story.

A few days after this, the news went around that the king's treasure chest had been stolen, and nobody could find the thieves. The grand vizier then thought of Faris, and suggested to the king that he send for him to help recover the stolen chest. The envious vizier did not make this suggestion out of any love for Faris or belief in his powers, but in the hope that Faris' claims might be proved false. So again Faris was sent for by the king. And again he was told that success would be rewarded, but if he failed he would lose his head.

Faris could not help feeling that this time he was doomed, but he remained calm and prayed for divine guidance. He asked the king to allow him forty days in which to catch the thieves. The king agreed to his request. When Faris got home he told his wife what the king had commanded him, and asked her what he should do.

"Do not worry, Faris," she said, "for all will be well. Do not leave the house, but stay at home. Every day for forty days I will have a chicken slaughtered for you, and cook it for the evening meal."

When the thieves heard that the king had ordered Faris to catch them, they were afraid; so they determined to find out if Faris knew that it was they who had stolen the king's treasure chest. That evening the leader of the thieves sent one of his men to Faris' house to see if he could find out anything. Under cover of darkness the thief listened at the window about the time Faris and his wife would be starting their evening meal. At that very moment Faris' wife had just put the cooked chicken on the table. As she set it in front of her husband, he said in a loud voice, "This is the first of the forty!" meaning, of course, that it was the first of the forty chickens and the first of the forty days.

When the eavesdropping thief heard these words he took fright, for there were forty thieves, and he thought that Faris was referring to him. He hurried back to his fellow thieves and told the leader what he had heard. But the latter did not believe him.

"You are imagining things," he said. "Tomorrow night I will send someone else to the house."

The next evening another thief was sent to Faris' house with orders to listen carefully at the window. As he got there, Faris' wife had just placed the second chicken on the table. Then the listening thief heard Faris say in a loud voice, "This is the second of the forty."

Without waiting to hear any more, the thief went back and reported to the leader what he had heard. The leader did not believe him, and resolved to go himself the following night to find out the truth. When he got there, the chicken had just been put on the table, as on the two previous evenings. Standing close to the window, he heard Faris say in a loud voice, "This is the third of the forty."

When the thieves' leader heard these words, he was convinced beyond any doubt that Faris knew who had stolen the king's treasure chest. Quickly he went back to his comrades and told them what he had heard.

"Brothers," he said, "we must go at once to Faris and confess that we stole the chest, and promise him that we will take it back to the palace. We will ask him to plead for us before the king, otherwise we shall all be put to death."

The same night, the leader went to Faris' house and confessed that he and his band of thieves had stolen the treasure chest. They were prepared, he said, to restore it to its rightful owner, on condition, however, that Faris should get them the king's pardon.

"You have done well to come here today and promise to restore the stolen chest," said Faris sternly, "for I was about to inform the king of the matter first thing in the morning. I knew that you and your fellow thieves had stolen it, from the very first day. Return the chest tonight, and I will put your case to the king when I see him in the morning. Though, on my life, rascals like you do not deserve the king's pardon."

On the following morning the treasure chest was found back in its usual place in the palace. Faris put on his best clothes and went to see the king. He explained how he had apprehended the thieves within three days of the theft, and ordered them to restore the chest to its rightful place. The king had the chest brought to him; he opened it, but found that nothing had been taken from it. So pleased was the king at having his treasure back that he gave Faris a reward of five hundred gold pounds, and handed him a written pardon for the thieves.

Faris took the money home to his wife. "I think it would be best," he said to her, "for us to leave this country for another, lest the king call me again and command me to carry out a task even more difficult than the last."

So Faris and his wife packed up their belongings and betook themselves to a far-off country where they lived quietly and happily to the end of their days.

The Story of the Boy Who Couldn't Keep Anything in His Head

Once upon a time there lived in a poor and remote village a boy called Mustafa. Everybody knew him; not because he was clever or handsome or brave, for he was none of these things. He was not even a liar as some children can be. You see, in order to lie, you have to remember things to lie about, but Mustafa couldn't even do that because of his forgetfulness. It was amazing how quickly he could forget what he saw, heard, or was told. As a result, people not only made fun of Mustafa; they also looked down upon him as an ignorant boy who could never learn anything.

Somebody said one day that if there had been a school in the village, Mustafa might have at least learned to spell his name, to which another villager replied,

"Mustafa will always be Mustafa. Even if we had one thousand schools, he would still be the same—he would probably have learned one thing only—how to forget one thousand times faster. And I'll tell you the reason. When the Almighty created Mustafa, he must have put into his skull the biggest sieve on earth, instead of a brain. That is why he cannot keep anything in his head."

The man who said this and the people who heard him should really have been more helpful and kind toward Mustafa, because it wasn't his fault if things slipped his mind. He didn't mean to be like this. He really did try to have a brain instead of a sieve in his head, but the trouble was that somehow his efforts always went wrong.

One day, for instance, his old granny who lived with him in the humblest hut of the village, called Mustafa and said to him,

"Come here, Mustafa, little son. I want you to go to the market and buy me twopennyworth of nothing. Here is the money—go now and get back with the 'nothing' as fast as you can."

"All right, Granny," said Mustafa, "I'll set out right away."

As he was hurrying to the distant market, Mustafa kept asking himself what sort of thing "nothing" was. He wondered what granny wanted to do with "nothing." Mustafa had actually meant to ask his granny about it, but, you see, being forgetful, he had forgotten to ask. However, he was also an obedient boy who loved his grandmother very much, and he wanted to get the right thing. After all, it would be very bad if he bought something quite different by mistake, and even worse if he forgot what granny had said and bought "nothing" at all. In order to keep the old woman's words in his head, he kept on repeating them aloud: "Twopennyworth of nothing, twopennyworth of nothing." But soon after, he forgot about the pennies, and carried on shouting, "Nothing, nothing, nothing."

Now as Mustafa was thus trying to remind himself of the purpose of his errand, he came upon two fishermen casting their net into a river. When they heard him shout, "Nothing, nothing," the fishermen grew very angry. They took him by the collar and gave him a sound thrashing.

"What do you mean by shouting 'Nothing, nothing'?" they said. "We have been here since early morning in the hope of catching some fish to sell at the market. Are you making fun of us? Aren't you ashamed of yourself?"

"I am sorry, big brothers," said poor Mustafa. "I was only trying to remember what granny told me."

"I am sure," said one of the fishermen, "your granny would not have wanted us to go empty-handed to the bazaar."

"What do you want me to do then?" asked Mustafa.

"Well, said the fisherman, "if you want to be a kindhearted boy, you should say, 'Let the fish come in tens and twenties.' Maybe your words will bring us luck and we'll land a good catch."

So Mustafa started to run again, this time shouting, "Let the fish come in tens and twenties. Let the fish come in tens and twenties." But he couldn't keep so many words in his head for very long. By the time he had reached an old stone bridge farther down the river, the fish had slipped out of his head, so to speak. He was now shouting, "In tens and twenties, in tens and twenties." The bridge led to a hamlet where a man had died that morning. They had washed his body and put it in a coffin. There was great sorrow among the friends of the dead man. His poor wife and children were following the coffin in tears, and leading the procession to the cemetery came an imam, a priest, who grew very angry when he heard Mustafa shouting, "In tens and twenties." He seized him by the collar and gave him a sound thrashing.

"What do you mean by shouting 'In tens and twenties'?" said the imam to Mustafa, who couldn't understand why he was being beaten.

"What have I done, Father Imam?" he kept asking. "What have I done that you should beat me like this?"

"Let this be a lesson to you," said the imam. "I hope the beating I have given you will drive the wickedness out of your heart. You must be wicked indeed to shout like that. You ust enjoy seeing people die. It seems that one death is not ᴨh for you—you want the people of this hamlet to die in ᴨ and twenties. You heartless boy, do you know that were granted there would not be a single soul ᴵet?"

ᴵng that an empty hamlet would deprive

him of his livelihood, belabored Mustafa with more blows.

"Oh please, Father Imam, don't beat me," said Mustafa. "I was only trying to remember what the fishermen told me."

"Fishermen don't go around wishing people to die in tens and twenties," answered the village priest.

"What should I do then?" asked Mustafa.

"When you see a dead man, you should say, 'May he rest in God's mercy and compassion.'"

So Mustafa forgot the fishermen and their advice and put into his head the words of the imam. A little farther on he saw a dead dog lying in the middle of the road. Seeing the dog, Mustafa said, "May he rest in God's mercy and compassion." But, as luck would have it, the village priest had followed him at a distance. On hearing Mustafa he gave him a great big smack on the neck.

"Oh, Father Imam," cried Mustafa. "Why do you hit me so? I was only repeating what you taught me."

"Stupid boy, don't you see that this is only a wretched dog. God's mercy and compassion are for believers."

"What then should I have said?"

"You should have said, 'Oh, it stinks, oh, what an awful smell,' or something like that."

Mustafa promised himself to remember this. When he reached the market he saw a public bath for women. He went in and found people washing themselves. He said loudly, "Oh, what a stink, oh, what an awful smell." Upon which a woman came and boxed his ears.

"Why are you beating me?" said Mustafa to the woman. "I am only saying what the village priest told me to say."

"A man of God would not say such a thing. He knows that cleanliness is next to godliness. People who wash don't stink, they don't smell awful."

"What would you have me say then?"

"You should say, 'Oh, what a sight for sore eyes.' "

So Mustafa forgot about the mercy and the compassion and the dog and the stink, and put the woman's words in his head. When he went out, he saw two men fighting. On seeing the fight, Mustafa said, "Oh, what a sight for sore eyes." The men stopped quarreling and, seizing him by the collar, gave him a sound thrashing.

"Why are you beating me?" asked Mustafa.

"We are beating you," they said, "because you seem to enjoy seeing us fight. You don't even know why we are fighting."

"I was only repeating what a lady told me. What will you have me say or do?"

"We don't want you to say or do anything. Just go away. We want nothing else from you."

At this, Mustafa suddenly remembered his errand. At the market he saw an old woman selling vegetables. He asked her what "nothing" was. The old woman, who thought she was about to have a customer, was disappointed and clouted Mustafa on the head.

"Well, I never," she said. "I can see that you belong to this district—how come you don't know that in our part of the world 'nothing' means salt? Such ignorance . . ."

Mustafa went and bought twopennyworth of salt and rushed back home. His granny, who had meant to use the salt for the wheat soup she was preparing, was terribly cross, because in spite of all his running and hurrying the boy was very late. When she caught sight of him, she emptied the soup onto the garbage dump and gave him two resounding smacks.

But Mustafa, being the boy he was, soon forgot about the beatings, the clouts, and the smacks he had received from various hands, and started playing happily by himself—and happiness never hurts anyone!

The Tale of a Proverb

Once upon a time there was a very just and upright king. So famed was he for his justice that even the birds and beasts knew of it.

Now, the birds in his kingdom used to lay their eggs in a very peculiar place, at the bottom of a well. They were no sooner laid, however, than a snake used to come along and eat them. This troubled the birds very much, so one day they made up their minds to complain of the snake's behavior to the king.

They all set out one morning for the king's palace, and when they got there they settled on the roof of the palace, filling every corner of it. The king and his vizier were puzzled by this, and wondered why the birds were behaving in this way, as nothing of that sort had ever happened before. After

130

a while the birds flew off in a body, and the king and the vizier decided to follow them. The birds led the two of them to the well, where they saw the snake eating the birds' eggs. The king and the vizier therefore killed the snake, so that from now on the birds were able to lay their eggs in peace and safety.

After some years had passed this vizier died and was replaced by another one who was neither wise nor good. In addition to this misfortune, there was a drought in the land, the crops were poor, and there was a shortage of money. At that very time the king wanted to build himself a new palace, for which he needed a lot of money. The vizier advised him to tax the people and take all the gold dinars they possessed. Those who refused to give up their gold dinars were put to death. But one woman wanted to keep the few golden dinars she had, yet at the same time she wanted to avoid being killed. So she resolved to hide the money in her dead husband's grave. One night she opened his tomb and put the money in the skeleton's mouth.

Ten years later the king wanted to find out if there were any people who still had gold dinars in their possession. So he had a very beautiful girl brought to the public market place of the city, and made it known throughout his kingdom that the man who possessed one gold dinar would be able to marry the girl.

The son of the woman who had hidden the money in her husband's grave ten years before, saw the girl, and at once fell in love with her and wanted to marry her; but he did

131

not have a gold dinar. He was very unhappy about this and told his mother. She then told him about the gold dinars she had buried. That night the son went to the cemetery. He opened his father's tomb and took the gold dinars from the skeleton's mouth.

Next day he went to the royal palace, taking with him a gold dinar. At once he was arrested and taken to the court of justice, where he was asked where he got the gold dinar from, since nobody was supposed to possess any of these coins. When he told the judges they ordered his mother to be seized. She, in turn, told them what she had done.

When the king heard her story, he grieved over the injustice which he had inflicted upon his people, and recited the following words, which later became a Tunisian proverb:

"We used to be so just that even the birds brought their complaints to us. But we became so unjust that people were forced to open the tombs of their dead."

The Donkey, the Ox, and the Farmer

So renowned was King Solomon for his great wisdom that people used to make long and arduous journeys to seek his advice and obtain knowledge of many things. Before the departure of his guest it was the king's custom to give him a costly present.

One day a rich farmer came to Solomon's court to consult him on a number of matters. When the time came for him to leave, the farmer refused the customary gift and asked, instead, if the king would teach him the language of the animals and birds. The king said that he could do so, but he warned the man that such knowledge was dangerous if used unwisely. Should he utter a word to any person of what he heard from a bird or a beast he would surely suffer death. Despite this warning the farmer was very insistent; so King Solomon granted his request.

On his return home the farmer overheard a conversation between his donkey and his ox.

Said the donkey, "Tell me, brother, how do you fare these days, and how does our master treat you?"

"By your life, brother," the ox replied, "our master treats me harshly. I spend my day in hard labor and toil while you do little in the way of work and eat the choicest foods."

Said the donkey, "I grieve for your sake, brother, and am indeed sorry for your lot in life. If you follow the advice I am about to give you, you will live a life of ease and comfort and be rid of all toil."

"I will surely take your advice," the ox replied, "for it is clear that you have my welfare at heart, and you are an astute person and a wise counselor. I shall do whatever you advise me."

Said the donkey, "This is my advice to you. When they bring you your straw and fodder tonight don't eat any of it, but lie down quietly. When our master sees you he will think your are ill, and he will not send you out to work in the fields. Then you will be able to enjoy a well-earned rest. This is what I do sometimes when our master rides me too hard."

The ox followed his companion's advice. When his food was thrown to him that night he declined it and lay down. The farmer then went away wondering what trick the donkey was up to. But later that night he went back to the stable, this time with his wife, and saw the donkey munching away greedily at the ox's portion. The man, recalling what he had heard earlier in the evening, laughed aloud at what he saw. His wife who, of course, did not know what was going on, was curious to know the reason of his sudden laughter. Her husband—having in mind King Solomon's warning—told her that he had just remembered something funny which had made him laugh.

The next day the farmer decided to punish the donkey for his sly trick on the ox. He ordered his servant to let the ox rest for the day and make the donkey do the ox's work as well as his own. At the end of the day the donkey returned to the stable tired and worn-out and exhausted from his day's toil. The ox greeted the donkey, praised him for his nobility, and thanked him for his kindness in enabling him to rest all day. The donkey did not reply, but silently repented of his stupidity and want of wisdom. The ox then asked if the donkey had heard anything from their master concerning them.

"Yes," replied the donkey, "I heard our master say that he is going to have you slaughtered to make your skin into leather. I fear for your life, brother."

The ox trembled at these words, and said, "I shall go to work in the morning."

When his food was thrown to him that night he ate it ravenously till there was not a speck of it left. The next morning the master and his wife went into the farmyard and watched the ox being led out of the shed for the day's plowing. When the ox saw his master he waved his tail and wagged his head and frisked about in a lively manner. The farmer roared with laughter at the ox's antics. This time his wife insisted on knowing the cause of his laughter. He told her that he could not reveal his secret to any living person on pain of death. But she pleaded and cajoled by turns, and threatened to go back to her father's house if he did not tell her his secret. Because of his great love for her the man agreed to sacrifice his life to satisfy her curiosity. However, before taking leave of this world, the farmer wanted to see his friends and relatives once more, so he sent for them to come to his house.

When they came he told them his story. In vain they urged the wife not to force her husband to reveal his secret but to leave well alone.

While they were thus talking the farmer went out of the house to wash. On his way he overheard his dog rebuking the rooster, who was eating his food with relish and joking with the hens.

"How can you make merry and eat in this manner when our master is about to die?" asked the dog.

"Is it my fault that our master is so stupid?" was the rooster's rejoinder. "I have twenty wives and I rule them as I will. I please one and anger another; no one dares disobey me. Our master has only one wife, yet he can't even control or manage her."

"What ought our master to do, then?" the dog asked.

"Let him take a stick and beat her with it," advised the rooster. "That will teach her not to plague him to reveal his secret."

When the farmer heard the rooster's advice he went back to the house and lost no time in carrying it out: his untimely end was thus averted, and he lived in happiness and prosperity with his family until his death at the age of a hundred and twenty.

Juha and the Dispute Over a Goat

Two men once had a dispute over the ownership of a goat. One of the men was large and fat, with a red face and a big black mustache, and a deep voice. He was called Hassan. The other was small, with a thin bony face, a short, straggly white beard, and a thin high-pitched voice, and his name was Ali. Each one claimed that the goat was his property. Since they could not agree, one of their friends suggested that they call Juha to judge between them. To this suggestion

Hassan and Ali agreed. So Juha was brought to decide the case.

"Now," ordered Juha, "let the two claimants and the goat be brought in before me so that I may judge between the one and the other."

Turning to Hassan, Juha said, "Now tell me your story."

"Well, your Honor," began Hassan, "I claim this goat as mine. It was given to me as a kid many years ago by a man who owed me a debt, and I took it in place of money. Since then I have brought it up and fed it and looked after it. One day it disappeared, and after much searching and inquiry I found it in the house of this miserable wretch with the whining voice and ill-favored countenance. When I charged him with having stolen my property, he abused me, and claimed that on the contrary the animal was rightly his and that I had stolen it from him. Your Honor, this man is a liar and the son of a liar!"

Juha then turned to Ali and invited him to state his case.

"Your Honor," began Ali in a thin piping voice, "may you be granted long life. The goat is mine, and this thieving rascal stole it from me. I bred this goat, it is one of a litter; I know it by its markings. I have dealt with goats all my life, buying and selling them. I can tell you the age and breed of a goat merely by looking at it. This man stole my goat because he had a grudge against me."

Having heard the two men, Juha looked at them both closely, then at the goat. After a few seconds he spoke.

"The goat belongs to Ali," announced Juha in a solemn voice. "It is well known that if two companions live together

for a lifetime they grow to resemble each other. So it is with men and some animals. The horseman, for instance, who is never parted from his horse, grows in the end to look like that noble animal in his bearing and his movements. So it is with the owner of the goat who has spent his life with goats and their affairs. Look, people, at these two men and the goat they both claim. Who most resembles this useful animal? The well-favored Hassan with his ample girth, jolly red face and big black mustache, or the thin meager Ali with his long bony face, white wispy beard and high-pitched voice? Does not Ali look like a brother to the goat?"

Having delivered his judgment, to the applause of the crowd, Juha left the court and mounted his donkey. As Juha rode off, Hassan, who was angry at having lost his case, shouted at Juha in derision, "Well have you spoken, for it is difficult to tell which of you two is the donkey!"

Juha at the Banquet

Juha was once invited to a banquet by the Governor of the city. When he had finished work for the day, he found that he had no time to change out of his working clothes, so he decided to go as he was. When he turned up at the entrance to the Governor's palace in an old pair of pants and a shabby

140

coat, the doorkeeper thought that Juha was a tramp and prevented him from entering.

"Look, you blockhead," he protested, "I am a guest at the banquet tonight. Get out of my way and let me pass."

"Go away, you loafer," shouted the doorkeeper, pushing Juha roughly. "You are no guest; you look like a tramp. Now be off with you before I cart you off to jail."

After some further argument Juha went home and changed quickly into a fine embroidered jacket and silk cloak. When he got back to the palace, he was shown in with every mark of honor and respect, and conducted to the head of the table and seated next to the Governor.

When the guests started to eat, Juha's neighbors at the table were astonished to see him take a plate of salad and pour it over his embroidered jacket; after which he dipped the sleeves of his silken cloak in a bowl of soup. When they asked the reason for this strange behavior, Juha's answer was brief and to the point:

"Since I am accorded the honor of sitting at this banquet on account of my fine clothes, and not for my own sake, is it not just that I should feed them rather than myself?"

The Magic Dagger

Once upon a time, there lived in a certain country a brother and a sister. The girl was called Mavi, and the boy Ali.

141

In those days there was also a magic dagger which everybody talked about. What kind of a dagger it was, or where it could be found, no one knew. But, it was said, this magic dagger could overcome every difficulty, transform the highest, most impassable mountains into the flattest of roads, and, so it was said, turn deserts into flowering gardens. All in all, there was not a thing that this magic dagger could not do. It was enough just to say "magic dagger" for running waters to stop running and for the most spiteful camel to turn into a docile animal.

Thus it came about that on one side of the world was the magic dagger, and on the other side were the people in search of it. Like all these many other people, Mavi and Ali left their village in pursuit of the dagger. On their feet they had iron sandals, and in their hands they carried iron walking sticks. They walked for days and nights. Neither fast rivers nor dry river beds could stop them. They crossed endless plains and tall mountains. They walked sometimes fast and sometimes slowly; they walked much and they walked a little.

But all this time they had not once laid eyes on the magic dagger, nor met a living soul who could tell them where it might be found. They grew hungry and thirsty, but they did not give up. Their resolution never wavered, nor did they ever think of retracing their steps. Parched mountains and dark forests failed to frighten them. Their hearts were set on one purpose—finding the magic dagger.

Their footsteps led them one day to a steep rock rising up to the heavens. For nights and days they looked and looked, but they could not find a way through the rock. Then, one early morning, they saw in front of them an old man with a long milk-white beard flowing down to his waist. Slowly the old man approached them.

"Are you jinns or sprites?" he asked Mavi and Ali.

"No, we are neither jinns nor sprites," answered Mavi and Ali. "We are humans just as God created us."

It so happened that the bearded old man was a dervish, a holy man, and he knew what the brother and sister were seeking in these parts where no birds flew and no caravan routes passed. But he held his peace and acted as if he knew nothing.

"If you are humans, what business have you in this place?" he asked.

Ali and Mavi told him.

"We have set out to find the magic dagger. Many months have gone by since we left our home and country. Now we have come to this rock which bars our path. Please show us the way so that we can reach the magic dagger."

The old dervish looked into the eyes of the brother and sister who were not afraid to meet difficulties.

"Dear children," he said to them, "since the day of its creation this rock has given way to no human being. Even if you waited till the end of your lives, your fate would be the same. The rock will not let you pass. You would be best to follow me. Wherever I go, you come too."

The old man turned around and started walking. Ali and Mavi followed him. As they advanced, the rock parted and let them through. A little later they found themselves at the edge of a plain which stretched as far as the eye could see.

"Here we are," said the old dervish. "We have arrived at this plain where no barrier stands in the way of your quest for the magic dagger. You must walk across this plain for many days and nights. You will then come to an iron mountain, which you must cross, and after a long journey a silver mountain will appear in front of you. That mountain you must also cross, but do not stop there. Allow nothing to delay you, but continue on your way. Your iron walking sticks and your iron shoes will begin to look worn-out, and this will be the first sign that you are nearing the magic dagger. Shortly afterward you will espy a golden mountain, which you must not cross. At the place where your path touches the mountain you will see a dry well. Into it you will fearlessly descend, because therein lies the way to the magic dagger. When you reach the bottom of the well, you will have left this world behind, and you will be in the land of jinns and fairies. I have no more to tell you. May your road be an easy one and may good luck hasten the end of your quest!"

Having said these words, the old dervish suddenly disappeared into thin air. Ali and Mavi were amazed, but also sad, because they were unable to thank the old man.

Brother and sister started their journey across the plain. They did as the old man had bid them. On and on they walked. They crossed the iron mountain, and then the silver mountain. They came to the golden mountain of which their saintly old guide had spoken. They found the well, which at first seemed bottomless; but then steps appeared, leading into

144

the darkness. They descended the steps, Ali in front and Mavi behind. Down and down they went, endlessly descending, until it seemed they would never reach the last step. At long last under their feet they felt the bottom of the well. There, facing them, was an iron door. They gave it a push, but the door remained closed. Ali and Mavi were now so very tired that they could hardly stand up, and to have another try at opening the door seemed impossible. But in a little while they heard creaking sounds and, lo and behold, the door was open and a dazzling light fell on their faces and shone into their eyes. In the doorway stood a girl as bright as the moon.

"Come in, little guests, come in!" said the girl. "You are welcome."

She took them through streets and gardens, the like of which Ali and Mavi had never seen before. Finally they arrived at a palace made of glass and adorned with beautiful tiles. Brother and sister were ushered into a lovely room with gorgeous carpets, gold candlesticks, and silver chandeliers.

The girl said to them, "Dear little guests, you are worn out. You must be sleepy, so please lie down and rest awhile."

She showed them a shining gold bedstead upon which were spread soft feathery eiderdowns. Ali and Mavi took off their clothes, laid themselves on the bed, and were soon asleep.

Now the girl who had brought them here was a fairy. She sent to the king of the fairies and gave him news of the arrival of Ali and Mavi.

"Let them sleep," said the king. "You will bring them to me when they awaken."

Ali and Mavi slept on and on, for seven whole years. One

day the young fairy came to wake them.

"I think you have slept enough," she said to them. "You must now feel fit and well."

When they woke up Ali and Mavi looked at each other in amazement, for Mavi had grown into a young woman as ravishing as an angel, and Ali was a lion of a young man. They tried to put on the clothes they had taken off seven years ago, and found that they would no longer fit.

"Do not worry," said the fairy. "I will have gold-braided garments brought for you."

When Ali and Mavi were thus dressed she took them to see the king.

"Dear young people," said the king, "it has been seven years since you came to this country. From the children you were, you have grown into beautiful youths. I know why you came here. You can see that we live in the midst of plenty. Whatever we wish is immediately granted. The costliest things in my palace are yours for the asking. Say but the word and my most faithful slaves will become your servants."

"Thank you, O generous king," said Ali. "I will never forget your kindness. But we cannot live away from our village. We should like to take the magic dagger and return home."

"Yes," said Mavi, "everything in your kingdom is beyond compare. To live here would be to live in beauty itself, but we cannot stay away from our own world and our own country. Show us how we may return to our village with the magic dagger, and you will have granted us the source of all bounties."

146

These words greatly pleased the king of the fairies.

"Well spoken, my children," he said to Ali and Mavi. "Had you decided not to go back to your own country because you found ease and comfort here, I would have liked you the less. Only if you have your country at heart can you have eyes to see, ears to hear, and hands to feel. You have proved your worth and your goodness. None has so far deserved to bear away the magic dagger, for none has thought or felt as you do. You shall have the dagger."

At these words the king waved his hand three times, and the third time the magic dagger fell upon the ground from nowhere.

"Take it," said the king, handing the magic dagger to Ali and Mavi.

When the king took the brother and sister to the bottom of the well he asked them how they would get out. In answer Ali and Mavi waved their hands three times, and away they went, leaving the good king behind.

And so ended their quest for the magic dagger.

Zohair and the Witch

There was once a boy called Zohair who lived with his family in a village not far from Baghdad. Just outside the village was a small house inhabited by an old witch.

One day Zohair happened to be passing by the witch's

147

house when he heard her voice talking. Curious to know what she was doing, Zohair stood on his tiptoes and peered through a window. He saw the witch talking to a jar she had put on the table.

"O my jar, O my jar," the boy heard her say in a crooning voice, "the source of all my pleasure. Let me have some good fresh milk. Fill yourself, my jar, fill yourself."

At these words the jar was suddenly filled with cool fresh milk. The witch then filled a large cup with the milk and drank it up greedily. Zohair watched all this spellbound from the window. What a wonderful jar, he thought, it must be magic. He determined to get hold of it somehow or other and take it home. Whilst he was thinking out how he could get it, the witch had finished her frugal meal and lain down on her bed to rest. Soon her snores filled the little house.

Zohair quickly crept through the door and, taking the now empty jar off the table, hurried home with it. He put it on the table and, remembering the witch's incantation, cried, "O my jar, O my jar, the source of all my pleasure. Let me have some good fresh milk. Fill yourself, my jar, fill yourself."

At this command, the jar began to fill up with cool fresh milk till it reached the brim. Zohair filled three cups and drank them one after the other. When he had had enough, he turned to the jar, saying, "Thank you, dear jar, I have now had enough."

But the jar took no notice. Milk continued to pour from its mouth in spite of Zohair's pleas for it to stop. He collected all the jugs, pots, pans, and buckets he could lay his hands on

148

and filled them all with the milk. Soon it was pouring all over the kitchen floor. By now Zohair was thoroughly frightened.

"Stop, jar, stop, jar!" he cried. "I don't want any more milk. I really don't want any more milk."

But the jar took no notice and went on pouring milk until the whole room was flooded. It rose higher and higher until it submerged the table and chairs, and spilled over into the other rooms of the house. The more poor Zohair shouted for it to stop, the more the milk seemed to flow, until the boy was in danger of drowning in milk.

He managed to get out of the house, and ran down the road, shouting at the top of his voice, "What shall I do? What shall I do? The house is drowning! The house is drowning! What shall I do?"

As he ran he heard a voice—he did not know where it came from—saying, "You did wrong, Zohair, to take the jar. Go back now to the witch and ask her forgiveness."

Zohair hurried to the witch's house. When he reached it, the old crone put her head out of the window and laughed in a loud cackling voice.

"I knew you would be back," she said, and cackled again with laughter.

"O witch," apologized Zohair, "I am very sorry that I took your jar. I know now I did wrong to take it. Please come back with me to my house, otherwise it will sink beneath the milk."

"All right, then," said the witch. "Bring me my boat from outside, so that we can row back to your house."

"But we don't need your boat," said Zohair, "we can walk back."

"Oh, no, we can't," was the witch's rejoinder. "Just take a look out of the window."

When Zohair looked, he saw to his astonishment that the street had become a river of milk. So he brought the boat from the back of the witch's house and they both got into it. The boy had to row all the way back. His arms ached till they could hardly move owing to the thick creaminess of the milk that flowed along the street. When they arrived at the house, the flood of milk had reached the top of the door, so they had to enter through a window. There they found the furniture floating on the sea of milk. Zohair pleaded with the witch to save his house.

"Have no fear, Zohair," the witch assured him, "your house will be saved, and it will be as it was before you took the jar."

So saying, she began to intone the following words in a crooning voice: "O my jar, O my jar, the source of all my pleasure. Hearken to me, O jar, hearken to me. The time of your return has come."

At these words, the milk ceased flowing. Soon the milk which was swirling all over the house returned gradually to the jar, as did the river of milk in the street. In the end, not a drop of the milk remained. After the house had been cleaned, the witch made Zohair carry the boat back to her house on his head.

"Let that be a lesson to you, my boy," were her parting words to Zohair. "In future do not take what belongs to other people, nor meddle with what does not concern you."

"Cast Thy Bread Upon the Waters"

There once lived a certain man of Jerusalem who had become prosperous during a lifetime of hard work and endeavor. He did a great deal of good with his wealth and dispensed charity to all those in need. When he grew old and felt that his end was not far off, he called his only son to his side, and told him he was to inherit all the wealth and goods that his father had amassed through the course of many years of industry. The son begged his father to give him a blessing before departing from this world.

"I have no blessing to give you, my son," said the old man, "but I would commend to you a priceless piece of wisdom which I would pass on to you. This you must treasure in your heart."

So saying, the father took up the Book of Ecclesiastes in the Old Testament, opened it, and read to his son the following passage: "Cast thy bread upon the waters; for thou shalt find it after many days." Soon afterward the rich man died.

After his father's death, the son put his inheritance to good account and took to trading and commerce for a livelihood, and in a very short time became a great and respected merchant. He traveled to many countries and visited all the great trading cities of the East, where he added to his riches by his skill and shrewdness in business matters. But so occupied did he become with trade and commerce that he soon ceased to care for anything in life except worldly success. He forsook the wise words and good counsel of his father.

One day, during his travels, he arrived at the great city of Constantinople, the capital of the Turks. He had never visited so fine a city before, and he marveled at its wonders, its fine streets, graceful buildings and lofty towers. He wandered through the squares and public places of the town, and never tired of watching the throngs of people going about their business or pleasure. One of his walks took him to the seashore where he came across two soldiers, armed with lances, standing guard over a stout wooden chest. Curious to know what great treasure was being thus guarded, he approached the soldiers and asked them what was in the chest they were guarding so carefully. "The mortal remains of a man," they replied.

The merchant wondered at this answer, and on his return to the inn where he was staying, told the innkeeper what he had seen and what the soldiers had said in reply to his question.

"What the soldiers told you is the truth," said the innkeeper. "The dead man, a Jew of this city, was an official in the household of the Sultan, and had served his imperial master faithfully for many years. But the other servants of the palace grew envious and jealous of him and spread false tales about him, and accused him before the Sultan of having stolen money from the imperial treasury. The Sultan lent ear to these false charges against the old official, and had him thrown into a dungeon where he died. After his death, his body was embalmed and put in the great wooden chest you saw being guarded by the seashore. And now our Sultan demands a huge sum of money, in gold pieces, from the Jews of this city before he will hand over the body to them for burial according to their rite. But they are a poor community and have not, so far, been able to raise the large payment in gold demanded by the Sultan."

When the merchant heard this sad story, he made a solemn vow that he would ransom the dead man's remains. He went to the palace and requested an audience of the Sultan. He told a member of the imperial household to inform the Sultan that a certain stranger had come to pay the money needed to free the body of the dead man for burial by the Jews of Constantinople. The Sultan ordered a servant of his household to have the foreign merchant conducted to him. On hearing what the merchant had to say, the Sultan asked him if he was a friend or kinsman of the dead man, that he should offer to perform this meritorious deed.

"No, Sire," replied the merchant. "I am from Jerusalem, and a stranger to your great city. When I heard the story of your dead servant, as related to me by the innkeeper, my heart

153

was moved to pity and I vowed to ransom the body."

The merchant's offer was received with favor by the Sultan, and the money, in gold pieces, was paid to him. The Sultan then told the merchant that if he had any request to make it would be granted him.

"I have a request," said the merchant. "Let Your Majesty command the Jews of this city to give the dead man the best plot in their burial ground, and let every person among them, young and old, accompany the body to its last resting place."

The Sultan showed surprise at this request, but he gave orders that it be carried out. That very day the body of the dead man was carried in a great procession, among a vast concourse of people, to the cemetery. There it was buried, with much ceremony and honor, according to the custom and rites of his people.

After the burial, the merchant left Constantinople and set sail for his native land. But hardly had the ship got out to sea when a great storm blew up and the ship sank. All those aboard were drowned, save the merchant, who remained floating on the surface of the water for a short while. Soon, however, he, too, began to sink, when suddenly a huge white eagle swooped down from the sky, plucked up the drowning man, and carried him all the way to Jerusalem. After setting him down at the gates of the city, the great white bird flew off.

On his safe arrival in his native city the merchant, as an act of thanksgiving for his miraculous delivery, dispensed charity among the poor and destitute of Jerusalem, and gave a banquet for his friends to celebrate his safe return to their midst.

That night the merchant's father appeared to him in a dream, and said,

"Know, my son, that the white eagle, which snatched you from the very jaws of death, was none other than the spirit of the man whose remains you ransomed and laid to rest among his own people. He heard your call in your hour of distress, and came to you in the guise of the king of all birds."

The merchant then understood that the words of wisdom bequeathed to him by his dying father were more precious than the most precious of stones.

Heart and Mind

Once upon a time Heart and Mind quarreled.

Heart said, "It is I who make a man a man."

Mind said, "It is I."

They did not bother to find anyone to adjudicate on the matter. They decided each to act on his own without the cooperation of the other, and chose to test this arrangement on a certain peasant.

The peasant chosen for their experiment took his plow and went to his field. As he was plowing a furrow, the plowshare suddenly jammed and, looking down, the peasant saw, lo and behold, a bronze vase filled with gold.

"What shall I do?" he thought. One part of him told him that he could do great things with this gold, that he could become a great man; another part told him that when the thieves got to hear of his find, they would come to steal it, and he would defend it and they would kill him. As he was wrestling with this dilemma he saw the judge of the province coming along the road, and decided that if he gave the gold to the judge, he could go quietly about his business without any fear of robbers. So he ran after the judge and asked him to come with him to his field. They were no sooner there, however, when the peasant's heart ceased to feel heavy, and his reason returned. He kicked some earth over the pot of gold, and said, "Sir, you are a judge, a learned man. Tell me, which of my two oxen is the finer?"

The judge, greatly annoyed, turned on his heel and left him. Then the peasant's mind grew dim, and his heart began to pound.

"Why did I not give him the gold?" he thought, anxiously. "Where should I keep it?"

He brooded over this problem all day, completely neglecting his work. As dusk was falling he saw the judge returning from the town. So he jumped up, ran before the judge, and implored him to come back to the field. The judge felt that there must be something wrong, and followed the peasant.

As soon as they reached the field, however, the peasant's reason returned.

"You are a learned man," he said. "Look at my field and tell me, did I plow more yesterday, or today?"

The judge decided that the peasant was queer in the head, and went off laughing. The peasant's reason seemed to follow him, for he sat down at the side of the field, dejectedly thumping his head.

"For goodness' sake, why did I not give him the gold?" he asked himself. "Where shall I keep it? *How* shall I keep it?"

He put the pot of gold in the satchel where he carried his day's rations, slung it over his back, and made off home.

"Wife," he said, "lock up the oxen, give them some hay, and put the plow away. I have to go to the judge immediately."

His wife eyed the satchel he had slung across his shoulder. There was obviously something in it, and he was not going to put it down. It was probably something very strange, she thought, and wondered how she could get a look at it.

"I look after the sheep and cows," she said. "It is not my job to lock up the oxen. Do it yourself, and then go where you will."

The peasant placed the satchel on the floor near the door, and went out to lead the oxen to the stable. His wife quickly opened the satchel, saw the pot of gold, took it out, and put in its place a stone of the same size and weight. The peasant came back, took his satchel, and hurried off to the judge's house.

"I have brought you a present, Your Honor," he said.

The judge opened the satchel and found the stone. He was greatly surprised, and no less so was the peasant. The judge grew very angry, but thinking there was something behind the peasant's behavior which merited investigation, he put him in a cell and posted two men at the door to see what he did, and hear what he said, and inform the judge. Inside, the peasant began to mutter and make gestures with his hands: the pot was this size, the spout was this long, the body was this wide, and there was so much gold in it. His watchers related all this to the judge, who ordered them to fetch the peasant.

They thereupon brought him before the judge, who asked, "What was it you were measuring with those gestures?"

Reason returned again to the peasant's head.

"Oh, I was measuring you, judge," he replied. "I was saying your head was so big, your neck so thick, your belly so round, your beard so long, and wondering whether you or our old billy goat was the fatter."

At this, the judge exploded with fury, and told his men to take the peasant away and hang him. They took him to the scaffold, and were about to pull the rope tight, when he said, "Wait! There is something I must tell the judge."

So they took him again before the judge.

"What have you to tell me?" he asked.

"I have to tell you, judge," said the peasant, "that if your men had pulled the rope any tighter, I would have been throttled."

The judge laughed and ordered the peasant to be released. He went back home to join his wife and his gold.

158